Realizing Mental Health

by

Roger Mills, Ph.D.

Sulzburger & Graham Publishing, Ltd.
New York

P.O. Box 20058
Park West Station
New York, NY 10025

ISBN 0-945819-78-1 Soft cover
ISBN 0-945819-79-X Hard cover
Printed in The United States of America

Contents

Acknowledgments

There are a myriad of people I need to genuinely thank for making this book possible. If I tried to mention all of them, I would take up half the book. First I want to thank my daughters, Ami Mills and Barbara Lally. Their uninhibited joy for living, their beauty and wisdom, have greatly deepened my faith in the human spirit and our hope for a brighter world. My wife, Clytee, for keeping me pointed in the right direction. Sydney Banks, for demonstrating and sharing the deepest potentials in all of us. George Pransky for his insights in breaking down the helping process.

I especially want to thank my editor, Caroline Otis, for her patience, tenacity and compassion. She tore up my writing and gave it back more readable and humane. Here insights about connecting with the reader with empathy for the human condition have added immeasurably to this book. I also want to thank everyone on the P.O.M.T.I. faculty, as well as the professionals involved with the Florida Center for Human Development and the Advanced Human Studies Institute. Each of these people added pieces or helped clarify the logic of this model in ways that made it richer and more beneficial to society. I would also like to express my deep gratitude to all the foundations, local, state and federal agencies who have, over the last decade, devoted resources and staff to the development of pilot programs and training in at-risk communities, in community mental health clinics, and hospital or educational settings.

I want to thank my family, particularly my mother, for their resiliency and unwavering support in this journey. Lastly, I want to express my deepest thanks to every one of our clients and students. It is from them that we have learned more and more about the real beauty and resiliency of the human spirit. It is from them that we have gotten an inspiring glimpse of our genuine potential as human beings.

Preface

The conclusion that people are inherently capable of mental health and resiliency is one of the most profound implications of the model of our basic make-up as human beings presented in this book. This new paradigm for psychological treatment and prevention is hopeful enough to be exciting. It is built on the encouraging premise that every person has a hard wired, inborn, innate capacity to use common sense, to enjoy and respect others, and to mature in a socially responsible way—regardless of their past or their circumstances. This model also explains how people come to lose touch with this birthright of mental health. More important, it helps them tap back into their inherent self-respect, hope, and wisdom. It provides a logical, practical model of human behavior that is inspiring in that it directs people toward their inner strengths and the resiliency of the human spirit. It has demonstrated high levels of effectiveness in applications to both clinical treatment and prevention.

Over the last fifteen years of empirical observations, clinical follow-up studies and pilot programs in prevention and education, my colleagues and I discovered something fascinating about the human mind. Apparently, the mind is designed to function by projecting our thoughts outward infusing them with consciousness to formulate each person's view of reality. While the mind will project any kinds of thoughts a person has, it has an innate propensity to regain a healthy outlook. It possesses a natural resiliency that provides powerful self righting mechanisms. Based on these discoveries we have developed a new paradigm concerning the nature of mental health and mental illness. This health realization paradigm connects thought, consciousness and resiliency in a new way.

The Basic Nature of the Mind

Throughout the history of psychology, theorists and researchers have debated over contrasting models concerning the most basic character of the mind. Psychology of Mind offers a relatively simple, understandable, practical, and logical description of how the mind works. In this paradigm, "Mind" is simply defined as both the source and the projector of thinking. It is also the source of our consciousness, which the mind mixes with our thinking in a way that in turn creates our unique experience of life. This process works in a way that determines how reality looks to each individual. Perhaps the most exciting of these findings is that the human mind has the capacity for projecting a profound inner wisdom, a healthy, mature psychological guidance system that all people share as a part of the human potential.

In this model, both mental health and mental illness are products of thought. In essence, the mind provides a psychological impetus or force that projects our thinking outward into consciousness in a way that takes on the appearance of reality. Because this impetus comes from inside out, it creates a seeming paradox. On one hand, life looks different to every person. Each individual's reality is unique to them. Yet at the same time, everyone seems to have the potential to access a common wisdom that brings an understanding about the human experience of life. This occurs because the process is always the same, each person's viewpoint is the result of a logical, predictable and definable thought process. Not only is this process understandable to us, as researchers and practitioners, but it is also understandable to our clients, and lay readers.

The Range of Functioning of the Mind

Psychology of Mind comprises a set of integrated principles that take into account the co-existence of individually learned beliefs and of higher-order feelings, insights, and wiser, healthier perspectives. The model describes how people learn self-destructive patterns of thinking while pointing the way toward a healthy, positive, and productive psychological vantage point. And it provides compelling evidence that every human being is capable of functioning from a healthy perspective that encompasses self-esteem and self-efficacy.

If the principles that underlie the Psychology of Mind model hold water, they provide a practical description of what causes emotional disorders and stress. The principles would then serve as the basis for new, more effective approaches to treatment and prevention—and for improved outcomes. In this book I will try to describe the impact of these findings while clarifying the differences between this model of the mind and other cognitive or thought based models. It is also important to distinguish this model from approaches that manipulate thought or recondition beliefs. One of the most exciting aspects of this model for us, in the way it has developed, is that it empowers people to experience volition in their own thinking. At the same time, an understanding of this approach acts as an immunity to the trap of trying to live up to, or be controlled by what others think.

I want to thank the colleagues who have helped me develop and refine these ideas by testing them in pilot studies and clinical treatment programs. Hundreds of professionals in the mental health field have now contributed immeasurably to the construction of this model and its applications across vastly different client groups. One of the things about which each of these practitioners and researchers would now agree is that thought is the most fundamental building block of everyone's reality, a common denominator. Thought is the key independent variable in the equation that links our everyday functioning as human beings to the quality of our lives.

The Central Role of Thought

Over the last two decades, the cognitive revolution in psychology revealed that thought is central to human psychological functioning (Beck, 1976; Bandura, 1982, 1989, 1991; Brown and Inouye, 1978; Lachman, Lachman and Butterfield; 1979; Seligman, 1975; Suarez, Mills and Stewart, 1987). Yet the cognitive schools have largely maintained a behavioral orientation. They argue for a strict focus on the contents as the only observable products of thinking—i.e., specific thoughts and behaviors.

As my colleagues and I explored how people move from unhealthy habits of thinking to healthier thought patterns, we saw that the thoughts that shape behavior are brought to life by consciousness; clearly, consciousness needs to be folded into this mix, too.

The Relation of Thought and Consciousness

In this new paradigm, "Mind" is analogous to a power source. It projects our thinking outward, flowing through consciousness to determine our perceptions. The result is similar to the effect that movie producers call "suspension of disbelief", a term used to impress on actors and special effects people the need to draw the audience into a movie as a realistic, engaging experience. Psychologically, a similar process creates the everyday human experience of life.

This model simply defines consciousness as the force that animates our thinking, making it come alive in our senses. It is the faculty that allows us to experience life. The way that thought and consciousness work together determines how reality looks to people, and at the same time, it enables people to become aware of their moment to moment thought process; to understand facts about their thinking. These facts include how people carry their past with them through time, and how to access their healthy, common sense thought process.

In exploring the link between thought and consciousness, we realized that people could have insights about their thinking; they could learn to distinguish their mind as the source of thought—and to distinguish between healthy and unhealthy thoughts. The results were very encouraging. People began to recognize that both their moods and outlook were changeable, and that these two things determined how they felt about and approached things. They became more patient and waited to address upsetting situations until they were in a positive frame of mind. They understood that everyone gets caught up in negative or self defeating habits of thinking, but trusted the resiliency of mental health enough to know that their good feelings, common sense and clearer perspective would come back.

The Potential Impact in Psychology

As my colleagues and I experienced these kinds of insights directly, we found that our lives changed profoundly, both professionally and personally. Our relationships with friends, colleagues and families improved tremendously. We found a new level of contentment, enjoyment and gratitude for the nicer feelings in our own lives. We found that these feelings were part and parcel of a healthier, less stressful frame of mind, emerging naturally and spontaneously. We started to appreciate even more the treatment and prevention potential in these discoveries, and we felt that we should find a way to teach our clients about the roles of thought and consciousness. We redoubled our efforts to find ways to assist them realize insights about the relationship of these elements to their day to day states of mind, to the roles that thought and consciousness played in shaping their lives.

The Innate Ability to Bounce Back

At the time we were arriving at these conclusions, a number of researchers were doing fascinating work in disadvantaged communities. Long term studies were revealing that a surprisingly large percentage of young people who had grown up in highly stressful environments and/or dysfunctional families rose above these conditions to become healthy, responsible adults—without outside intervention (Benard, 1991; Garmezy, 1991; Hawkins, Catalano and Miller, 1992; Linquanti, 1992, Mills, 1991a, 1992b, 1993; Werner and Smith, 1987).

These outcomes led us to an interest in resiliency, the natural ability to rebound from adversity and regain equilibrium. It seemed to us that people's innate resources for health just might be stronger than the effects of negative circumstances or pathology. After all, the human body routinely produces chemicals that fight off disease and restore health. Why shouldn't the same principle hold true for the mind? My colleagues and I posited that by teaching people to recognize their own mental immune system, they might be able to fortify it.

During the same period, research in educational psychology was revealing that even alienated, disadvantaged students could motivate themselves to learn and change. In a positive state of mind, students exhibited the capacity to reflect, enjoy learning, have insights, and grasp the underlying principles behind problems. They also developed a healthy, long-range view that reduced drop-out and delinquency rates substantially (McCombs, 1991; McCombs and Marzano, 1990; Mueller, 1992; Rutter, 1989; Ryan, Connel and Grolnik, 1993; Deci and Ryan, 1985).

Initial Pilot Programs in Health Realization

Beginning in 1987, I received grants from federal, state, and local government agencies and foundations to apply our findings about mental health to prevention and early intervention programs in hard-core, inner-city environments. In his recent book, Legacy of the Heart, which chronicles the strength and survival capacity among at-risk youth, the well known educator Mueller (1992) described the task of helping people transform their lives: "Your challenge is not to keep trying to repair what was damaged, [but rather] to awaken what is already wise, strong, and whole within you, to cultivate those qualities of health and spirit that are available to you in this very moment."

This quest was the focus of our prevention and early intervention programs. The positive results of our initial program surprised even us. Communities plagued by soaring school failure rates, endemic drug and crime problems, violence and gang warfare turned themselves around. Today, many of the teens who were in the streets dealing drugs have finished high school, some are in college. Their parents are employed, and their younger siblings are doing well in school. In addition, residents banded together to take back their neighborhoods, to write their own grants and implement their own programs for community development. These outstanding results have garnered national recognition and media attention for our programs, which are now being replicated in places like the South Bronx, Oakland, California, and high-risk communities in other states.

In Chapter Seven, I go into greater depth in describing how these efforts were actually carried out in high risk communities, how they were linked to this health realization model and the results of three to six year outcome evaluations of these pilot programs. I recognized that if this approach could yield promising results like these with people in the worst of circumstances, then our findings should be applicable in all areas of mental health treatment and education. Indeed, our clinical results have shown similar promise.

Clinical Follow-up Studies

Thus far no rigorous, control group studies have been completed using this treatment method. However, some clinicians using this model in a treatment setting have collected preliminary data worth noting. In one such study with 25 court-mandated DUI clients, a clinic found that after treatment, 13 people quit drinking completely while the remaining clients reduced their drinking to a manageable level. All reported substantive improvements in their family life, social life, and job performance in ways that would be predicted by this model. (Stewart, 1987).

In another study, 82 clients of six different therapists at three treatment centers reported that their distress symptoms had disappeared or abated to the point where they felt they could solve their problems on their own. The average length of therapy in this study was 14 sessions per client (Suarez, 1985; Shuford, 1986; Shuford and Crystal, 1988). And the results seem to endure. For example, a six-year follow-up of 85 clients treated for a variety of anxiety and depressive disorders revealed that 86.9 percent showed sustained, positive change in mood and appearance, while 82.6 percent reported higher self-esteem and positive changes in their marriages and other personal relationships (Bailey, Blevins and Heath, 1988).

In 1989, Minneapolis-based therapist Joe Bailey followed up on 231 clients, half of whom had been treated for depressive disorder. The majority reported significant reduction in symptoms. Of those diagnosed with severe depression, 73 percent reported "very significant" symptom reduction. Other patient follow-up studies have reported equally promising results with schizophrenic and dual-diagnosed clients (Bailey, 1989; Ringold, 1992). In our follow-up interviews with therapists trained in this approach, we found the vast majority reported significantly improved outcomes, were more hopeful about their work and were planning to continue their training and applications of this model (P.O.M.T.I., 1994).

Fishing For Understanding

"Give people fish and they will eat for a week. Teach them to fish and they will eat forever." Giving people fish by treating the symptoms of their pathology—the congestion of a cold, the counterproductive behaviors associated with depression—may alleviate discomfort, at least for a while. However, it does not cure the problem by addressing it at the source.

Traditionally mental health treatment has focused on what practitioners of this approach would probably now view as symptoms—specific behaviors or thoughts. Through our findings, my colleagues and I discovered that a more solid mental well-being seems to come from nurturing the capacity for insight and for health—by teaching people to fish for understanding. As people learn to recognize the difference between contaminated, learned thinking and the insights born of their inner wisdom, the mental immune system kicks in to ward off emotional distress.

It was extremely exciting to glimpse the possibility that mental health is our default setting. Wisdom, common sense, and clarity are as free and unconditional as the air we breath, as the sunshine that lights our days. When we allow it to, mental health holds sway in our lives. The most tricky aspect of this process is gaining an ability to let go of an attachment to conditioned thinking that may seem real and compelling at the time. Then all we need to do is relax and let the mental immune system do its work, yet often this may seem like the hardest thing to do. Realizing we can do that is half the battle. Understanding how this process works is the focus of our work, and of this book.

This book is intended to serve anyone who is interested in helping people function with increased well being, self-esteem and maturity. The findings related here should be useful to social workers as well as to psychologists, family therapists, and professionals in all areas of human relations work. The book should also prove valuable for those who would like to see our society function in a healthier way, one in which every citizen has equal access to self-worth and happiness.

I am writing this book as a documentation of a journey; a journey that began for me and my colleagues in the mid-nineteen seventies while engaged in research on primary prevention at the University of Oregon. I have not included many references to other worthwhile research or theories. I want the reader to be able to follow the same trail of logic that we followed in our quest for a new paradigm for understanding mental health and mental illness.

While you read, please try not to interpret these ideas in the framework of existing theories or approaches. I know that this will be hard to do. Instead, take them for what they are, noticing their inherent logic and their implications for the practice of both mental health treatment and prevention. At the end of the book, I have included a list of suggested readings. These references are intended to illustrate the scope of the research and findings in all areas of psychology, learning and resiliency that reinforce, that point toward and amplify the implications of the ideas presented in this book.

In my next book, I plan to go into more detail, in a more academic manner, on how these insights relate to the evolution of psychological thought, to research findings and to developments in other fields that have led us toward a greater understanding of thought and consciousness. This book however is aimed at both lay and professional readers; at students of human behavior who have maintained the hopeful view that we can understand the human mind in a way that provides hope for individuals, for society and for the planet. Let us begin.

CHAPTER ONE

Discovering a New Paradigm for Mental Health

A new paradigm in any field calls for articulating our ideas about cause and effect. Only in the process of finding the words to describe a new model does the model become real enough to be understood and put to work. In this book, I will define the principles that comprise the new paradigm which my colleagues and I have come to call Psychology of Mind. These principles touch every facet of human behavior.

The "we" in this book refers to me and the other professionals who have been researching and refining Psychology of Mind over the last 20 years. Back in 1973, a small group of us began this exciting journey with the help of a federal research grant. We set off to find both preventive and clinical approaches that would deliver more consistently positive outcomes. We felt that such an investigation could move psychology forward. As co-primary investigator, I tried many different approaches in pilot programs that we carried out across the state of Oregon.

In 1977, we stumbled across a set of ideas that seemed to provide an overarching logic. This logic reconciled apparent contradictions across different approaches to therapy (Mills, Odum, and Wappes, 1978). We were actually like many researchers who were looking for one kind of thing and suddenly stumbled onto a set of clues that led us in an entirely new direction. Although we were looking for a route to mental health, we were looking at it from the more traditional viewpoint, as a problem of reducing illness or attacking the pathology. A person outside the field helped us take a fresh approach, suggesting that we might study what healthier people had learned or knew that kept them healthy.

At first, we were pleasantly surprised by our findings. Gradually, we become extremely excited as we observed our clients move beyond chronic self-defeating patterns of behavior and emotions to enjoy their lives and become more stable and productive citizens. As we followed these clients over a five-year period, we noticed that the change in them was greater and more enduring than that produced in conjunction with other forms of interventions. These findings aroused new hope and enthusiasm in everyone involved in this research, and we have learned much from one another ever since.

The follow-up investigations we conducted have given my colleagues and I fresh insights into what constitutes mental health. We found it increasingly easier to teach clients how to engage healthier states of mind and to understand the effects of their negative or self limiting habits of thinking. As we analyzed the results of our research, we became increasingly hopeful about the possibility of creating a simpler, more direct route to healthy functioning in our clients.

Over the last decade, we have been following this route; the paradigm that emerged from our data gave rise in the1980s to a new approach to psychological treatment and prevention, to human relations training and mental health education. By now, many mental health practitioners have adopted this approach, including experts in chemical dependency, family violence, and chronic emotional disorders. To date, their results have been very promising and the potential for improved outcomes in every aspect of therapy and prevention is exciting.

What Led Me To This Research

In college, my main academic pursuits were math, science, and engineering. These interests led me into the field of astrophysics as a pioneering area of science. By the time I received my degree in aerospace engineering from Princeton University, however, I had become more interested in psychology and anthropology, having taken these subjects as electives. I was fascinated by the wide variety of cultures, particularly the wide ranges of belief systems and behaviors across different groups. In fact, some behaviors that were considered pathological in one culture in others were respected or almost revered. The main distinction seemed to be that people thought differently about these behaviors.

As a research assistant in a major aerospace laboratory, I had seen the extent to which the psychology of organizational and professional cultures influenced the politics, personality conflicts and working relationships in even a scientific research institute. Often people's cultural biases and personal insecurity interfered with the lab's research and development agenda. Brilliant minds spent valuable time in squabbles over who had more research assistants or equipment or space. Technicians sabotaged expensive test equipment because they resented the treatment they got at the hands of primary researchers. It seemed that human factors interfered with research goals and that how people thought about themselves and others made a huge difference in how effectively they were able to work together.

In order to rethink what I wanted to do with my career, I accepted a teaching stint in a Taiwanese university, which led to my work with the United Nations as an economic development consultant to small Taiwanese companies. I soon saw that my "clients" had a limited frame of reference; their inability to see their companies as anything more than small family concerns was the main factor keeping them out of the burgeoning export sector. It became clearer to me from my experience with clients like these, and from the aerospace lab, that feelings and attitudes were what motivated people to move themselves forward—or held themselves back.

I began to recognize that psychology was as much a core science as anything else I had studied. People's thinking and emotions determined how they acted, how they made decisions, and how they treated others. Their thoughts and feelings determined their social and cultural values, their success at work, and the extent of their community involvement.

I decided to pursue this line of inquiry. In 1968, I entered a new, experimental, interdisciplinary Ph.D. program at the University of Michigan to pursue an area called "social and psychological processes." Most of my course work and clinical work was in organizational, community, and social psychology. I also took clinical training and courses in anthropology, sociology, public administration, planning, and educational psychology.

As part of my research fellowship, I worked at the Institute for Social Research on a ten-year longitudinal study of Detroit area youths. It followed a large cohort of students from the elementary grades through high school, testing a wide range of influences on their lives, including their upbringing, their community environment, their school experiences, their relationships with peers and teachers, societal forces, the media, and other variables that might affect their mental health and personality development. Although the data we gathered was copious, no clear, unambiguous relationship emerged between the students' mental health and the theoretical variables we were studying—variables derived from a combination of then-current theories of child development and environmental influences. Could it be that other factors were more important?

After receiving my Ph.D., I became executive director of Oregon's first federally funded community mental health center and joined the adjunct faculty of the University of Oregon. I soon discovered that few of our clients enjoyed any permanent improvement. Readmission rates for the hospital-based treatment programs were a discouraging 85 percent. Results were similar for our other programs, including drug and alcohol treatment and family counseling.

In meetings with directors of other centers around the country, I found that these statistics held true at the national level, too. Clients either stayed in treatment for 20 to 30 years, or they returned frequently for help with the same or similar problems.

My colleagues and I were eager to find something more effective in assisting people function self sufficiently. Under the auspices of the University of Oregon, we applied for and received a five-year grant from the Innovative and Special Projects Branch of the National Institute of Mental Health to study "primary prevention." The federal grant was matched by the Oregon State Department of Mental Health. Our aim was to discover how to help people function without long-term dependence on the mental health and social service systems. We set out to pinpoint the facets of treatment and prevention that were most effective.

Letting Go of The Past

At first, the structure of our research was predicated on what we had learned in graduate school. There, of course, "the past" had played a starring role. Our textbooks held that each human being is the product of his or her past, and thus has attitudes, values, and behavior patterns that are immutable. Psychological problems, then, arise from a complex interplay of internal psychic forces, heredity, and the environment.

There were variations on this basic theme. The psychoanalytic model saw adult personality and behavior as the result of psycho-sexual conflict among the id, the ego, and the superego. Social learning theories posited that personality and behavior are molded from lifelong patterns of external reinforcements. Other schools of thought attributed repressed reactions to earlier traumas as the root of mental dysfunction.

Then there are the more recent cognitive studies, which drew parallels between the brain and the computer. In these models, information from past experience was programmed into the brain, where it could be accessed to interpret present events. The brain, it seemed, could not distinguish useful from useless information, handling thoughts about self-concept in the same way it processed thoughts about how to ride a bike. So, if the brain told people they weren't attractive or couldn't hold a job, they would behave as if these thoughts were truth—and get results to match, thus confirming their negative expectations.

Whatever the variation, all of these theories emphasized that people are the product of their past. However, there was little consensus within the field on the factors that help people overcome the traumas of their past in order to change the way they think and act.

Evidence of Mental Health

Both the outcomes of our pilot programs in primary prevention and our clinical observations hinted that all people are sometimes in rational states of mind, regardless of their past. At these times their feelings and behavior weren't as influenced by past traumas or conditioning. At other times they reacted to things more irrationally. We wondered if there was a variable or a dimension of functioning we had missed that could account for these mood shifts? Could we learn more about how healthy states of perception come about so that we could teach clients something practical and useful concerning these states?

Recognizing Thought as The Vehicle

From the research that produced the "cognitive revolution" in psychology—and from our early research in Oregon—we began to suspect that each individual's past is carried forward through time via learned habits of thinking. Yet none of my graduate psychology courses had ever named thinking as a central dimension of human functioning. Nor were any of the psychological disorders we had studied linked to patterns of thought. By the late 1970s, our research was giving us clues that "the past" was not what caused self-destructive behavior, rather, the culprit appeared to be negative habits of thought.

The Missing Link: Thought + Consciousness

Early in our study, as we experimented with a wide range of approaches, we stumbled onto something intriguing. We noticed that people who had learned something about how their thinking affected their behavior were making tremendous gains in their lives—without as much effort as it took with other models it seemed. We had not introduced new beliefs or asked them to change their beliefs. Yet, something other than their conditioned habits of thought had entered into perception. This something else had given them perspective on their thinking, a more conscious awareness of their ordinary thought process.

We pursued this finding further, developing some rudimentary ways to teach people about their thinking. We saw our clients apply these insights to recognize that their negative feelings about themselves stemmed from their learned habits of thought. They gained the ability to distance their thinking about their situation from the situation itself and to see the past as the source of their habitual way of thinking about events rather than as a source of permanent damage; this ability in itself had remarkable effects.

These clients recognized that their learned beliefs caused predispositions to respond behaviorally. They could see that many of their attitudes were self-confirming—and often self-defeating. They also had learned to distinguish objective, clear thinking—what would normally be called something like common sense—from their conditioned habits of thinking, noticing that one kind of thinking seemed familiar and generated reactivity, while the other kind of thinking was more productive and motivating.

After learning to distinguish thoughts generated by ingrained beliefs from thoughts produced by healthy common sense, people showed sustained improvements in their overall levels of self-esteem, creativity, and motivation, and in the ability to maintain close, respectful relationships with others. We weren't sure just how these people had arrived at this new level of maturity and wisdom, yet we could not deny the results. We became more excited about our work than ever.

Programming Thought Versus Awareness of Thought

In the early 1970s, cognitive theories from the work of Bandura, Beck, and others posited that human beings are passive receptors whose negative beliefs could be reprogrammed via external stimuli. These psychologists developed methods to supersede existing negative patterns with positive patterns of reinforcement. Based on our findings, however, my colleagues and I felt that the idea of reconditioning clients toward more positive thinking was only a limited solution, and different from what we were observing as healthy common sense.

Again and again, we were seeing pronounced change in people as they became aware merely that they have a thought system and that it determines the quality of their perceptions and behavior. We were seeing that people who learned how their thinking works could use this knowledge to alter their moment-to-moment perceptions. It seemed to us that people didn't need to be reprogrammed through external stimuli when they were capable of deprogramming themselves simply by recognizing themselves as the source of their own thoughts. These realizations moved them into the driver's seat of their own thinking.

As we worked with psychiatrists who were drawn to this approach, we observed that even extremely disturbed people could grasp that their behavior was the product of bizarre thoughts produced in frightened states of mind. They learned to recognize their paranoia as a thought-generated nightmare of their own making, not the "real thing." This understanding helped them sustain more rational and functional thoughts and behaviors, more of the time.

In many of our pilot groups, we used no other intervention strategy or counseling method besides this "awareness of thought" approach. Yet the outcomes we were getting were noticeably better and more enduring than in our other pilot programs. The treatment process was also faster, simpler, and required less reinforcement. These clients didn't feel the need to attach themselves to any therapeutic rituals or support groups. They were living happy, productive lives without giving much time or thought to maintaining their new status.

Interviews with our clients yielded important clues as to what they were actually learning. They saw clear value in putting the past behind them and framing it in a common-sense perspective. They did not carry scars from past events; they recognized whatever had taken place, but weren't drawn to dwell on past traumas and mistakes. They could accept others' differences and not take things personally. They exhibited little envy or regret.

Because they trusted the buoyancy of their good feelings and a positive outlook, they tended not to become discouraged by mistakes or setbacks. They were consistently hopeful and creative in addressing life's problems. Observing these people, we started to recognize that the mind has an innate propensity to right itself. We observed, over and over again with our clients, that our minds are always attempting to regain a perspective of mental health, just as the body's immune system works naturally to fight off disease and restore physical health.

The people we followed showed a unique capacity to thrive at work and to enjoy more happiness and peace of mind in their personal lives. Type A personalities relaxed without losing their energy and motivation. People who had been unable to hold jobs gained stable employment or launched their own businesses. Chronically depressed individuals learned to enjoy life more. Alcoholics stopped drinking. We knew we had hit on something important, and we wanted to learn more.

Congruence With Other Research

As our research progressed, two significant research trends in psychology began to dovetail with our findings. In the field of learning and motivation, researchers were finding that all students—even the most disengaged—were motivated and eager to learn, at least from time to time. The researchers posited that this intrinsic motivation was not contingent on the usual rewards of approval or grades, but rather on inherent, higher-order thinking capacities that encompassed an ability to reflect and an awareness of the thinking process, a natural curiosity and unforced enjoyment of learning and discovery.

In the prevention field, the results of longitudinal studies done over 20 to 30 years revealed that a surprisingly large percentage of young people who grow up in dysfunctional families or destructive environments rise above these conditions to become healthy, responsible adults—without the aid of any structured intervention. In the prevention and child development literature, these results gave rise to the notion of resiliency—the idea that people can rebound and regain their equilibrium. These findings have since become the basis of health promotion approaches that build on people's innate resources for health, with the view that these are stronger than their pathology.

Our respect for people's innate capacity for understanding and wisdom increased exponentially as we saw clients exhibit unprecedented qualities of judgment and perception. As we incorporated our findings into new pilot programs, we found that people of all backgrounds were able to develop an awareness of their thinking that enabled them to rise above their habits to gain a healthy, big-picture perspective. We began to suspect that we, as mental health professionals, might need to rethink how we weigh our clients' capacity for mental health.

Our Capacity for Understanding

As our work progressed, we came to suspect that all human beings share the potential capacity to understand and take charge of their own thinking, emotions, and behavior in a way that psychological theories had not accounted for adequately. This understanding was helping hundreds of people in our pilot programs and studies to change their old habits of behavior forever.

Locating a Common Denominator

My colleagues and I had been schooled to believe that different problems required separate methods of intervention. None of the problem-specific techniques we knew had singled out thought as the link to all patterns of emotion and behavior, as a common denominator across all facets of human behavior. Yet this approach seemed to work across the board. As we disseminated our findings to various branches of the mental health field, clinics and treatment centers reported significantly improved outcomes with all kinds of clients. In turn, practitioners in hospitals, universities, and chemical dependency programs began to develop and refine new applications of this health realization paradigm.

Healer, Heal Thyself

As we put our approach into practice, we saw that it helped our fellow professionals as well as our clients. Psychology has been a profession with high burnout rates due to the frustration of fighting uphill battles to help clients, with all too few success stories to show for the effort. But as this approach began to yield promising results with relative ease, therapists told us they were experiencing the kind of excitement and enthusiasm for their work that they hadn't felt since graduate school. Their home lives were improving, too. Our students reported similar changes—along with a growing excitement about launching careers in the mental health profession.

Indeed, we noticed that our students were applying these insights in their own lives. They were leaving their clients' problems at the office and enjoying their families. They recognized and dropped deep-seated resentments, assumptions, and habits of self-pity or commiseration. They grew more relaxed and self-assured. We noticed a strong connection between how well therapists applied these insights in their own lives and how well they were able to help their clients.

As our research continued, we realized that it was time to suggest some new building blocks for psychology. We began to suspect that every dimension of psychological theory and practice was connected to the human capacity for thought and to how our thinking combines with consciousness, moment to moment to inform perception. As we recognized that people are more than the sum of their beliefs, we saw potential for taking mental health treatment, education, and prevention in a new, holistic direction. We saw that building on the core capacity for health was more fruitful than focusing on pathology.

My colleagues and I have encountered a few obstacles over the last 20 years. When we first reported our findings, many psychologists thought that what we were exploring was too simplistic. In fact, we were frequently sidetracked by these considerations ourselves. After the first stage of our work was complete, my colleagues and I still disagreed as to the significance of these ideas and their relationship to the outcomes we had observed. Yet we stubbornly followed the trail of results, clinging to Albert Einstein's axiom that any true breakthrough brings simplicity and the ability for generalization. We felt we had found a way to truly help people, and we felt a professional obligation to learn as much as we could about these dynamics and to share our findings with our profession.

It seems that the way new knowledge occurs in any field is that both preexisting and new data become reorganized in a different way, at a higher level of logic. This new logic accounts for patterns that previously seemed like confounding aberrations. Any higher level of organization provides a logical set of common denominators that make the complexities seem simpler to understand.

That's why I have written this book. In it, I will reveal what we have learned about the principles that form the backbone of Psychology of Mind. I will explore how mental health professionals are using these principles for treatment and prevention. And I will explore the potential of this approach for addressing pivotal social issues such as poverty, prejudice, and environmental concerns.

I will describe how this approach is working with individuals in clinical settings and how it is working with groups in community-based prevention programs in inner-city environments plagued by crime, drugs, delinquency, and hopelessness. I will share our many exciting success stories, along with our vision for the future of this simple, yet incredibly effective, transformational tool. I believe that you will be as impressed and excited as I have been by people's ability to harness their inner resources to turn around their families, their communities, and themselves.

CHAPTER TWO

Toward New Building Blocks for Psychology

As any field of endeavor moves toward quantification as a science, it is essential to pinpoint the basic principles that cause or predict the phenomena being studied in that field. For example, when scientists discovered more basic building blocks of matter—the protons and neutrons (the nucleus) and the electrons around the nucleus—it opened up a new level of accomplishment in physics and related fields. By understanding these elements in different combinations, physicists could form new substances and tap into the energy available in every material object. Since that time, physicists have identified more fundamental principles concerning how matter and energy interact at sub-atomic levels. These advances have led to the current revolution in computerization, micro-electronics, and telecommunications.

Similarly, our findings led us to propose that all individual and collective human behavior can be traced back to the combination of three basic building blocks of the human psychological make-up. For practical purposes of discussion it seems most helpful to look first at three basic building blocks. These building blocks are: mind, thought, and consciousness. In this view, the human mind functions as a kind of power source, projecting thought and consciousness. In other words, the fabric of each person's subjective reality is woven from the cloth of thought combined with consciousness. In a state of perception uncontaminated by learned, conditioned thought, our observations have consistently shown us that a mind will produce a healthy, common sense thought process.

Thus any description of how the human mind works must account for resiliency and the intermittent but continual reoccurrence of rational thinking. Our observations also indicate that each person's subjective experience is projected from within using the vehicle of thought. In other words, what any person makes of the situation they are in now, especially their habitual interpretations of what it means, comes from inside and is projected out by mixing thinking with consciousness in a way that makes up that person's psychological reality.

A simplistic, short hand, version of the proposed building blocks of human psychological functioning include three basic principles:

1) The most useful and important way to view the mind is as the source of thinking and consciousness. The mind projects thought as the vehicle to create our experience of "reality." It mixes thought and consciousness in the process of producing our subjective reality. In this model of psychological functioning, the human mind is capable of projecting either conditioned thinking or thinking that produces insight, common sense and wisdom.

2) Thought is the function that creates images and perceptions in the brain. There are two qualitatively distinct kinds of thoughts in the human experience, conditioned versus original or clear, insightful, common sense thinking.

3) Consciousness is the faculty that brings our thoughts to life and makes these images appear real. In other words, consciousness is the ingredient that is added to thought to make our version of things take on the appearance of reality.

This book offers a compelling logic model, based on these three principles that explain every state of mind, every kind of emotion, reaction, and behavior. This theoretical framework is logically and systematically linked to the interaction of these three common elements. They are the underlying principles of this emerging health realization paradigm that we have come to find applicable to alleviating a wide range of psychological maladies. While it may, on the surface, appear simple, it provides an overarching theory of human behavior that is logically consistent and can incorporate data from a wide range of theoretical perspectives. Just as the principles that describe atomic structure form the basis of all matter, our findings have led us to consider these principles to have strong potential for providing a new theoretical foundation for the science of psychology.

Such a statement, at first may appear simplistic and even insulting to the reader's intelligence. I would only ask that you wait, suspend judgement at this point and attempt to understand how the wide ranges of human behavior described in each of the following chapters are tied back into the logic of these principles throughout this book. In this chapter, I will describe how we define each of these principles. I will attempt to describe what we have learned to date about how they are linked with one another, and how they affect our experience of life. I will explore their implications for rethinking the nature of mental health and for finding the most fruitful direction for therapeutic treatment. In subsequent chapters, I will develop the applications of these basic ideas to the role of the helper, to counselling and therapy, to prevention and motivation, to stress, to relationships and to other areas of research in psychology.

Principle #1: Mind

The "Mind," from our observations, is most usefully defined for the field of psychology as the source of thinking and of consciousness. It combines these elements to determine how we experience and evaluate life, including our emotions (how we feel about things), and our perceptions (how things look to us). The mind, simply defined, is a tool that enables humans to think, to actually produce thoughts they then use to evaluate or interpret their experiences. Every human experience is a result of this process.

While many other researchers have written about cognition, with remarkable accuracy, and others have written about consciousness and the human experience, the model presented here provides an understanding of the immutable link between thought and consciousness. Without thought, humans would not have an experience of any external reality. Without consciousness, there would be no experience of reality. When the two are combined, projected outward by mind, we have what could be called the human experience of reality.

The key variable in this equation appears to be the kinds of thoughts we mix with consciousness. The quality of our thinking determines the quality of our experience of life. Our observations have shown us that people sometimes evaluate their situation from a frame of reference of their conditioned thoughts; what they have been taught to think by others. At other times, they seem able to put aside or bypass these kinds of thoughts and see things with a fresh set of insights and more profound, objective judgements that have nothing to do with their own past developmental history or personal biases. These kinds of observations have led us to conclude that the mind is also the source of a more profound natural intelligence that all human beings seem to share in common.

This definition may seem simplistic, but heuristically it is very operational. In practice, the working of the mind might be compared to the operation of a movie projector. The mind projects our thoughts outward to construct our view of life from the inside out. If we had never seen a film before, we might possibly walk into a theater, look toward the screen and think that what we see on the screen is real. At that moment, we wouldn't understand that, or how, the movie projector (our mind) was processing a reel of film (thought) to create the illusions before us (the picture we see).

Because it is the projector of our thoughts, the mind operates before our thinking. Since all we can experience is the view of reality the mind projects, it is impossible to capture and describe the nature of the mind accurately. The basic problem is that what we see is always a product of the experience that the mind is projecting via thought. Because we cannot see the projector, but only the thoughts it processes, we can only infer what the mind is and how it works. That's why any conceptual model of the mind can only be a piece of film, not the projector.

Just as different reels create varied images on the screen, so do different thoughts create vastly different experiences of the very same situation—and because of the way our psychological projection process works, all of the experiences seem equally "real."

For example, one person who has moved into subsidized housing may be grateful for shelter and hopeful about her prospects to finish her education and get a better job now that her housing situation is secure. On the other hand, another new resident may perceive that by moving into public housing, she is sinking downward and will never escape from the quagmire of poverty. Because of the dynamic relationship between mind, thought and our consciousness, each of these two different versions of the same reality can seem equally real and compelling to each of these individuals.

In a second example, one job applicant is nervous before the interview. He tells himself that his nervousness will make him lose his composure and blow the interview. This can, of course, become a self-fulfilling prophecy. Another applicant is equally edgy, but tells himself that his nerves will provide the shot of adrenaline he needs to impress the interviewer. One person had a thought or an insight that helped to make the situation more manageable. In this case too, each person's view of that reality looked like the right one to them. Without deciding who is right or whose reality is wrong, who is more likely to get the job?

The mind provides us with both the thinking ability we need to evaluate life, and the capacity to understand how we use that ability. Whether we use it in our best interests or use it in ways that become self destructive or self limiting depends on our degree of understanding regarding how the mind works in this respect. We have found that once people grasp the nature of this thought process, and the function thought plays, they tend to use their thinking more productively.

Principle #2: Thought

Every human being is thinking, 24 hours a day, every day of the year. Our thoughts are always in motion, connecting us to life and filling it with meaning. In fact, thinking and the thought process are common denominators that work the same way across all human beings, before the contents of different ways of thinking. In this section I urge the reader to merely look at the role or function of thought itself, rather than the contents of how different people learn to think. I am attempting, in this section to describe the process and role of thought as a guiding principle, as an independent variable, rather than as a product or dependent variable.

Thoughts assume many forms. They can be reactions to an event or stimulus occurring right now. They can be memories—stored thoughts about past events, relationships, and sensations. They can be beliefs or values—patterns of thinking that have become so ingrained that we don't even notice we're thinking them. Or thoughts can be insights—lightning flashes of creativity or knowledge that seem to come out of nowhere.

Our physical senses are hard-wired to thought in a basic connection that cannot be severed; whatever our senses experience is made real only by thought. When we feel pain, for example, thought translates the signals from the nervous system and transmits them to the brain. Thought locates the source of the pain and determines what we should do about it. If we were knocked unconscious and someone pricked us with a pin, we wouldn't feel it. Thought is the most fundamental link to our senses. It brings sensations, when interacting with our consciousness, to life.

Thought not only allows human beings to recognize what we experience in the material world; it also allows us to imagine experiences of the senses and to react accordingly. When we think of our favorite foods, we experience hunger and begin to salivate. Our thoughts turn to a lover and we experience desire. We have anxious thoughts about our work and suffer headaches or heartburn. Music sounded only in the brain can stir the soul thanks to the artful intermediary of thought. And the famous neurosurgeon Wilder Penfield was able to electrically stimulate different areas of his patients' brains to trigger vivid hallucinations of earlier experiences that included strikingly "real" smells and physical sensations.

The point here is that everything we experience—in real life or in the imagination—can be tied to our thoughts. Thought is the command key for the biological computer we call the brain. And while we usually aren't aware of the endless river of thought flowing through the brain, we are aware of the perceptions, emotions, and behaviors that are the products of our thinking. How things look, how we feel, and what we do are the effects of thought. Thought is the fabric of our life experience that fills the gap between a person and his experience; it is the interpreter of life. As such, it is important for us all to understand the nature of thought and the role it plays in our lives—as distinct from the content of our thoughts. From observing the ups and downs of our clients we concluded that there are two noticeably different thought processes through which thoughts are generated and used to evaluate our daily lives. Everyone at times exhibited a rational, common sense, insightful thought process. When in this thought process, people were less self conscious and had practical, relevant ideas and insights about things going on in their lives.

When asked about this thought process people experienced it as relatively effortless and spontaneous. They might make the statement that they had nothing on their mind. Often, when people had new insights that helped them they stated that they weren't thinking of anything in particular at the time. We found that peoples' experiences in this state of original thought were fresh, insightful, engaging and productive. The other thinking process seemed to be related to what cognitive psychology calls conditioning. In this process people are applying associations or ideas gained from past experiences to evaluate their present circumstances.

Conditioned Negative Thinking, The Barrier to Mental Health

The central role thought plays in creating our experience of life came into focus during the first year of our research programs in Oregon. In listening more carefully to our clients, my colleagues and I saw how their learned habits of thinking were affecting their perceptions and behavior from moment to moment. We observed that all of us, clients and therapists alike, carried our separate views of reality around with us via nothing more or less than habitual ways of thinking. Some habits of thought are useful. For example, remembering how to drive a car, or find our way to work, to read, write and do math. Other habits of thought seemed counterproductive. These were thoughts that impacted our self concept, or that determined what we felt chronically insecure about in our lives, or that produced habits of hostility, resentment, poor-me feelings or discouragement.

These habits took the form of fixed attitudes, of habitual preconceptions, expectations, prejudices, and beliefs. How do these belief systems come to be? Babies are not born with conditioned negative thoughts about life. Soon thereafter, however, they are exposed to the ideas, opinions, and perceptions of those around them. They pick up their habits of thinking from the community and society in which they live, and then imprint these ideas in a process called conditioning.

As stated earlier, conditioned thinking in itself is not necessarily bad or limiting. Without it, we'd spend most of every day relearning how to tie our shoes or drive a car. But just as we internalize useful information, we do the same thing with beliefs that are not helpful at all, such as "I can't learn" or "Nobody likes me." As soon as this information is programmed into the brain, it too becomes our personal "reality."

For example, in families where the parents tend to respond to frustration with anger and violence, their children pick up this habit, too. If parents always worry, so do their children. Anger and worry are what constitute "normal" for these families. Young children don't know any better, so they tend to program, and to take seriously, how the people around them view life. These basic patterns of thinking and responding are those that get programmed into their brains at the deepest level. People then tend to develop behavioral styles or patterns that they feel will help them deal with life given how they have learned to think about things. One of our clients for example at the clinic in Miami, where we were doing follow-up studies, stated that his dad had told him it was a dog-eat-dog world, that he should watch his back and look out for number one. As a result he approached most situations with mistrust and suspicion of the people involved, even his friends and partners, throughout life.

If this programming is strong enough, or comes at an early age, so that it is basic, then these children may believe that this reality is the truth, is the only way of looking at things that is possible. Consider murderers who show no remorse. It isn't necessarily true that they are callous, heartless human beings. Rather, they have become conditioned to think in such negative, hopeless ways that they cannot tolerate their own thoughts. As a result, their "reality" is devoid of any real satisfaction or hope. They unwittingly use their own thinking to create a hell for themselves, and then fight that self-generated hell with their behavior. Like fish in a fishbowl, they think their little bowl of pain is the whole world. In this kind of hell-hole of conditioned thought, the best they may see to do is to take revenge on a seemingly hostile world.

Just as mud clouds the water in a fishbowl, so does our conditioning contaminate our flow of thinking. Contaminated thoughts affect our lives through our perceptions. Just as tinted glasses color everything we see and block out some hues, conditioned thinking is a filter through which we view the world. This belief system or mind-set can feel very "real."

Belief Systems Create Self-fulfilling Prophecies

Beginning in 1987, my colleagues and I received a series of grants to launch drug and delinquency prevention programs for at-risk, inner-city youth living in public housing in Miami. When we interviewed these young people, we found that they had developed self-defeating belief systems. By the time most of these kids reached first grade, they already felt their teachers were against them, they mistrusted all adults, they felt they would never make any real friends at school, and they felt they had to behave violently to earn any respect in the world. Their self-esteem was low and hope for a better future was at a minimum. Buying into this type of belief system lowered their moods, turning depression, hostility, and fear into a daily routine. These

thoughts and feelings colored their view of the world and their interactions with the people around them.

When we worked with these kids and their parents to help them understand their beliefs, they started to reorient themselves to their own thinking. They recognized these habits, with relief, as nothing more than their own learned self-defeating thoughts. From this realization, they were able to let go of many of these destructive patterns and experience the warmth of hope. They reengaged their natural interest in learning and intrinsic motivation. In this book I go into the intervention program and the results we observed in our prevention and early intervention pilot programs in more detail in Chapter Seven.

These young people felt the way they did for a reason, of course. Many of them were born into culture of poverty where constant discrimination and hardship are the norm and family violence and rejection are rampant in the community. We found it to be highly understandable when youth developed negative attitudes and responses toward society or their immediate environment. Nevertheless, we found that their day to day level of mental health was contingent not on the experience itself, but on the way they learned to hold the experience in their thinking. Some youth from the same housing projects, the same environment and the same family background enjoyed school, were motivated and able to learn. Others were alienated, hostile and turned off by school. The more contaminants present in their belief systems, the darker their moment-to-moment outlook on life—and vice versa.

In the course of our research, it became clear to us that there is a big difference between circumstances and the way people view or respond to those circumstances. If the mind is functioning in a way that produces negative thoughts, dark feelings and self-destructive behavior are also part of the package. Conversely, when the mind is generating positive, creative thoughts, positive feelings and behavior will follow, regardless of the specific situation. It was these inner resources that many high risk youth in the resiliency research had used to overcome adverse circumstances.

So, when misfortune strikes, we can, understandably, react from anger, fear, depression, or self-pity. Or we can rise to the occasion, and by not letting ourselves take things so personally, allow our natural common sense to deliver insights on the best way to make things better. We all admire those who seem to be able to do this naturally. It is exciting to glimpse the possibility that we all have this potential in us.

We found a direct correlation as well between mood states and the ability to handle adversity productively. This understanding of moods provided a link to how people can use their capacity for insight and common sense, even in adversity. Simply put, when people are feeling positive they have more common sense. It is often difficult for people to see that they can regain a more positive feeling without first changing their circumstances since most of us believe that our circumstances are what make us feel good or bad. Most people believe that they can't feel better until they are doing better. In fact, we found that it's the other way around: people tend to do better once they feel better, regardless of their circumstances. While this shift in perspective is not the magic wand that will lift people out of miserable situations, it does provide the wherewithal and motivation to change for the better.

Original Thought and Common Sense

In studying these two distinct kinds of thought processes, we recognized that the original thought process delivers common sense, insights and understanding. It is in essence a clear psychological vantage point that we would call mental health. Yet the field had not recognized fully the therapeutic value of this thought process, because it is natural and ordinary. Like our breathing, we don't really notice it when it is working. It is effortless and automatic. The conditioned thought process was more easily identifiable and describable, as it is how everyone has learned to use their mind. It is more effortful and conscious as we are actively analyzing and figuring things out in this mode.

We also observed that everyone, potentially, can realize that he is the thinker of his own thoughts, and thus the architect of his reality. This objective understanding, along with the recognition of the two different thought processes, helped people tremendously. This type of understanding offered new possibilities for addressing the continuum from dysfunctional to functional psychological states.

Indeed, once the kids we worked with in our pilot programs began to discern their own habits of thought and how these beliefs shaped their negative outlook on life, they became more motivated and used better judgment in class, got along better with their classmates, and were less susceptible to peer pressure. In the first year of this project, we witnessed a 75% drop in discipline referrals, and after year two a comparable drop in juvenile justice incidents, a significant increase in school attendance, and a drop in the failure rate from 64% to less than 12% at the middle school level. Three years later, drug and delinquency arrests had dropped still further. Most of the students who had been dropouts had reentered school and some were attending college. In addition, the teen pregnancy rate at the middle school had fallen by almost 80%.

Thinking Creates Reality

As my colleagues and I examined the results of our pilot programs, we realized that the way thought functions in life had been invisible to us before because all of us were functioning after the fact of our thinking. We professionals were no different from anybody else in that we had developed specific attitudes and beliefs. Instead of framing our thoughts in perspective—as the unique way each of us had learned to think about things—almost all of us saw our individual thought patterns as the one and only reality.

Most adults tend to react automatically from their thoughts, without questioning whether or not another perspective exists. We have labeled this tendency as being "set in our ways" or "you can't teach an old dog new tricks." What exacerbates this all too common syndrome is that others' response to our habits of thinking, feeling, behaving tends to reinforce those same habits.

For example, if a man feels that all women are untrustworthy and he approaches women with this mind-set (never recognizing that it is a mind-set), he will always have trouble developing close relationships with the opposite sex. Surprise, surprise. Similarly, if a teacher expects certain students to be slow learners, they will be. Yet, we observed over and over that these same students do just fine in classes where teachers expect them to excel.

These examples show how our habitual thoughts are routinely validated by our behavior. This realization brings to life an old saying. More often than not, "what we see is what we get." As a result, trying to change counterproductive behavior in ourselves or others is like trying to get the tail to wag the dog. Behavior is the tail, but the dog itself is thought. Every behavior is the result of a thought about what something means to us. People always act on how things look to them. When things look different, their behavior will be different.

At first, this understanding of thought seemed too simplistic to us because it failed to account for all the intra-psychic dimensions of traditional theories. Then it occurred to us that those theories had been hypothesized from the *thinking* of theorists. The experts who were teaching people their concepts could certainly make a compelling argument based on their own beliefs. Clients who respected this expertise then tended to buy into the "professional" interpretation of their own experiences and examine their lives from the theorists' frame of reference or belief system.

As we considered how our "expert" opinions affected what clients perceived to be the cause of their problems, we saw our potential to do inadvertent harm. Psychologists too often convinced clients that because they were products of their personal history, their mental disorders were fixed traits or character disorders. We suspect now that this isn't necessarily true, and that the field may have made the characterological explanation of psychological functioning more complex than it seemingly needed to be.

But if we could see this, then why couldn't everybody else? Why don't most people see how our thinking influences our behavior? The answer is that when people are caught up in the cycle of thought, perceptions, emotions, habits, and familiar outcomes, they are at the mercy of the feelings generated by this conditioned frame of reference. In other words, their conditioned thoughts and feelings keep them from seeing the forest for the trees.

Principal #3: Consciousness

When I taught in a Chinese university for three years, my own cultural beliefs were such a strong habit that it took a long time for me to adjust to different ways of thinking about what was normal and appropriate. Although I knew intellectually that "odd" behaviors were nothing more than cultural differences, I often found myself upset, judgmental, and sometimes overwhelmed by these differences. Thank goodness my old habits of thinking lessened in importance in my consciousness, and my outlook eventually shifted to illuminate a new "normal" as I became more secure and comfortable in this environment. That shift had nothing to do with intellectual knowledge. Rather, it was a gradual but fundamental change to an entirely new outlook that has helped me many times over to feel comfortable in other cultures.

Consciousness can be a term that is confusing, as it has been used and approached in such a wide variety of ways. We are told that there are many different types of consciousness; e.g. self consciousness, race consciousness, male or female consciousness, class consciousness, higher consciousness, etc. What seems to make these states of consciousness different is the thoughts that are, in each instance, mixed with consciousness. Consciousness is constant, thought is the variable.

In the Psychology of Mind paradigm, "consciousness" has a quality of pure awareness. It does not, in and of itself, have any content. Yet it gives us the ability to notice things, to experience the contents of our external world. If we did not have consciousness we wouldn't notice anything at all. Human beings must be conscious to experience life. Consciousness may be likened to a spotlight. Whatever pattern of thoughts we put in front of the light, are the thoughts that become illuminated. If the spotlight of consciousness illuminates garbage, garbage is what we see. If it illuminates a garden, we see flowers in bloom.

Consciousness has no content; it has nothing to do with what we see, rather it is analogous to the light itself, the capacity to be aware. Our thinking, on the other hand, is like film in the projector (mind) that passes in front of a light and is projected outward to form our personal perceptions. In the projection process, thoughts are mixed with consciousness to determine how we view our lives.

Another way of understanding consciousness, in this model, is that it is the faculty that makes the images produced by thought appear real to our senses. If we think of the sour taste of a lemon, our tasted buds react as if we had just eaten a lemon. Psychosomatic patients report extreme pain without any physiological basis. On the other hand, even hospital patients pain will often diminish if they are distracted from it by engaging their minds in conversations with visitors.

Whatever thoughts act as perceptual filters through the spotlight of our consciousness depend on what kinds of thoughts are most on our mind. If we are hungry, for example, we notice every restaurant on the street. If we are thinking about buying a car, we watch traffic with far more interest than usual. If we are seeking a mate, we keep an eye out for potential candidates everywhere we go. Thought creates images in the brain; consciousness is the power that makes these images appear real to our senses. Our conditioned ideas about significance often determine which thoughts we make important; in turn; the thoughts we make important determine whether we are feeling positive and healthy or hostile and hopeless. When people learn how the thought process works, they have more choice over which thoughts are illuminated and brought to life via consciousness. People can learn to ignore or lessen the impact of those thoughts that are contaminated by our negative conditioning.

The Interaction of Thought and Consciousness

What stood out in those clients who improved the most through our pilot programs was that their understanding of how their mind mixed thought with consciousness illuminated the way thought worked in their lives. They understood how to shift their attention from what they thought to how they thought. They could see that the power to think was a neutral vehicle that brought beliefs to life, irrespective of the contents of those beliefs. This new understanding of the thought process enabled them to bypass their belief systems.

Let's look at an example drawn from the therapy process. A young man referred to our clinic had been valedictorian of his high school class, but flunked out during his first semester in college. He returned home feeling almost catatonic. When he opened up and began to talk, he said he didn't feel he could survive and have any self-esteem unless he maintained the number-one status he had earned in high school. He was extremely anxious about the stiff competition in college.

We helped him by showing him how his thinking process worked and how he had created thoughts that were self-fulfilling prophecies of defeat. He came to realize that he had made these thoughts so important that they had overwhelmed him. He understood the role thinking played in creating his stress and anxiety—and this new awareness he had of the whole process, which was now all within his understanding, awakened him to how that process works.

After a period of treatment, the young man realized that he didn't have to live up to his self-imposed standards of self-worth. He said he thought he could make it in college now without having to be first in his class. As his beliefs diminished in importance, he began to enjoy school and was soon making straight As again. His natural interest in learning, curiosity, enthusiasm, and intellectual capacity returned automatically as soon as he made the shift to a less insecure state of mind and eased the pressure he had imposed on himself.

In another case, a client who was depressed about her unemployment felt too bad to look for a new job or go out with friends. Once we helped her see her thoughts as a conditioned pattern of thinking, she felt more hopeful and got on with her life. People who were insecure in relationships realized that their expectations of failure didn't have to be self-fulfilling prophecies. Clients with drinking problems recognized that they drank too much because they felt insecure. We also noticed that people who did not improve their functioning right away tended to use their beliefs as their reason. They seemed to already know why things would not work out.

From cases like these, we suspected that all human beings can become conscious of their thought processes in a way that makes their thinking itself clearer and more insightful. The next questions then became: What is it that lets people move into a state of awareness before their thinking occurs instead of after? How can people realize that they have power over their thinking when they are in the grip of their beliefs?

Reconnecting With Innate Intelligence

We wrestled with these dilemmas for a long time. When we asked our more aware clients for answers, they said they had come to their understanding via insights. Some of these "a ha!" moments delivered truisms: "I realized that it wasn't helping me to dwell on the past." "I recognized that I was working too hard to enjoy my life." "It hit me that the only person I can truly change is me." At any rate, these insights felt significantly different from their conditioned ways of thinking, although they both came in the form of thoughts.

I spent many sleepless nights struggling with the distinction between learned patterns of thought and insights. As I reviewed the literature on insight, I came across the case of a mathematician who discussed his frustration after months of grappling with a difficult problem. Finally, on a day when he abandoned the challenge to spend time with his children, the answer suddenly hit him like a bolt from the blue. When we asked around, we found that our clients came to their insights in much the

same way. They relaxed and suddenly glimpsed their habits of thought from an altogether different vantage point.

We started to hypothesize that there is a universal human intelligence that is the source of insights. It isn't the type of intelligence that can be measured with IQ tests or grades; rather, it can be described as common sense, good judgment, maturity, objectivity, and mental clarity. This intelligence is automatically available whenever people step outside their habits of thought, we figured. Engaging this state of mind allows positive capacities such as creativity and self-esteem to surface. It enables us to see the world from a "big picture" perspective, to not take things personally, to exercise common sense and uncommon wisdom. It gives us hope.

Gradually, I realized that whatever we perceive, whatever we feel, and the way we behave seems to depend on how we mix conditioned thinking with those thoughts produced by our native intelligence. When that intelligence comes to the fore, we access a psychological perspective that I call "mental health." Every human being seems to have access to this deep intelligence, irrespective of individual differences or past history. Apparently, even schizophrenic patients can enjoy a common-sense state of mind from time to time. We also noticed that this healthy state of mind is buoyant; it tends to resurface as soon as people loosen their grip on negative thinking.

Mental Health, Our Default Setting

My colleagues and I wondered why the field of psychology had never emphasized how people's innate intelligence seems to come and go in relation to their moment-to-moment state of mind, just as the thermostat in a house signals the heating system to switch on and off as the temperature in the house rises and drops. When people normally confront things about which they have insecure thoughts, they tend to become negative or insecure. This occurs when the thermostat switches on their conditioned thoughts, feelings, and responses. When people grasp the connection of this change in state to thought, they relax and feel better. Their resiliency thermostat then switches on creativity, common sense, and a mature perspective.

Why had we not focused on this capacity in looking for cures or improving our treatment methods? Why hadn't we noticed sooner that people function better in the present when they are not dwelling on their past or agonizing over their problems? One reason was that we had been trained to look for pathology and to take people's negative feelings, their self-destructive patterns of behaviors, and their self-defeating thoughts more seriously. We had learned to discount positivism as less real or meaningful than negative feelings and experiences. Sometimes we discounted good feelings as "denial." We missed logical implications of the fact that a great percentage of people raised in dysfunctional or disadvantaged families did not exhibit those same problems in their adult lives. Or a well known statistic that many schizophrenic patients who were diagnosed in adolescence experience spontaneous remission and live more normal lives in their later years. Only recently has the field of prevention, for example, taken an active interest in the concept of resiliency, the idea that people have a self righting capacity.

Now we are starting to acknowledge the phenomenon of innate resiliency, the ability to bounce back and overcome adversity. We have begun to study the characteristics of resiliency. These characteristics have led us to question approaches in psychology proposing that people had to work through their problems before they could feel better. As we questioned this assumption, we found that taking people into their negative past tended to cause them to recreate the same pain over and over, producing states of mind that were still dysfunctional rather than helping people put their traumatic experiences behind them once and for all.

Our work showed us more and more clearly that this core state of mental health and resiliency has nothing to do with "coping skills." It is not achieved through analysis or manufactured by willpower. It is not automatically engaged by building a client's ego or self-image. Rather, it comes as naturally as breathing. It is so natural, in fact, that often we only notice it in its absence.

The Foundation for a New Treatment Approach

Taken together, these principles of the mind, of thought, and consciousness, explain how the human mind works and allow for the precious ability to change. My colleagues and I saw that the true value in this approach is that we didn't need to study ways to alter the way people think, but rather help them to gain power over their thinking process and its effects. Using the three principles as our framework, we understood why placebos often are effective—if you believe that something works, it works. And we realized that it was highly likely that people could produce their own "cures," depending on the strength of their beliefs.

We envisioned the therapy process as looking something like this: We assist people to understand the role of thought and to distinguish between the two distinct types of thought processes. Clients then learn how to tap into their innate intelligence, which delivers insights and perspective. They use this new awareness to change their habits of thoughts, find a healthier frame of mind, and change their behavior. When our clients realize that an emotional disturbance is a state of mind rather than a fixed personality trait, they are able to drop their attachment to negative, self defeating habits of thought and rebound to healthier moods more readily.

The other side of this coin was that the applications of these ideas were of course more difficult than the theory itself. Everyone is attached to their beliefs, and in most clients, they are not cognizant that their self destructive behaviors had anything to do with their beliefs, or even with thinking itself. We had to carry out clinical trials and learn how to make these insights seem relevant to our clients experience of life. We had to learn how to help clients point themselves in the direction of having their own new insights about their lives.

We noticed, initially, that if we treated people as healthy and showed confidence in their healthy side, they gained hope and managed things better. This is where, inadvertently, traditional therapy limits itself by its biases. When we treat people as if they are one and the same as their problems—the embodiment of their pathology—they tend to become more and more "diseased." When someone believes what the experts say and this thought assumes reality via consciousness, it "locks in" as his experience of life.

If people are labeled as a certain personality type and begin to see themselves that way, they tend to become more and more that way. We began to understand why people often emerge from prison more hardened than ever before. We recognize a link between the way mental patients are treated in institutions and their diminished ability to function after they are released.

We found that by seeing people as basically healthy, and by pointing out that side of things, people become awake to that side of themselves more, and used their resiliency more consciously. In some ways, whatever we focused on and made important was what the client noticed and what seemed the most important to them.

In flipping the coin to our new approach, we have no wish to blame therapists for perpetuating their clients' problems—and sometimes making matters worse—through pathology or problem focused methods of treatment. We realized that the role thought plays in mental health has been hidden and that therapists have failed to see the seed of harm we can plant when we label people as certain personality types. Not realizing how thought and consciousness interact in the moment to determine perception, we didn't recognize the havoc that might be wrought from telling our clients they had been permanently damaged by a trauma. We just didn't know any better. We were taking people's reality from their past as a given, not recognizing that they recreated that reality every moment via their habits of thinking.

But after our results strengthened the case for our hypothesis about thought, my colleagues and I felt the time had come to transform our practices—to devise a form of therapy that could, in some ways, be seen as diametrically opposed to what many of us had done before. We concluded that we could help people much more by teaching them to elicit their own intrinsic health, rather than encouraging them to explore their dysfunctions. Instead of offering new, even positive forms of conditioning, we felt it would be more helpful to teach them that they are much more than the sum of any kind of conditioning, that they already held the keys to mental health in their own minds. Rather than trying to help using our understanding, we found we could help more by showing clients the route to their wiser, clearer psychological vantage point, to their capacity for understanding.

CHAPTER THREE

Thought, Feelings, and Personality

In this description of the basic functioning of the mind, thought is the main independent variable. Thought is the most causal factor with which we have to work. The mind, working like a projector, is a constant. It will project outward whatever thoughts we are having. In this sense the mind is a neutral projector. Whatever thoughts we put in the projector are what will come out as our view of reality. Consciousness is also a constant. We are always conscious of something. Consciousness is like the light in the projector. It illuminates whatever film is put into the projector. The power of our consciousness is that it can make any thought appear real if we subject it to the illumination that consciousness provides. Thus in this chapter I really want to talk most about thought. Thought is the variable in the equation that links reality with consciousness. Hopefully this discussion will shed some light on how thought, emotions and what we call personality are logically connected.

It may seem to a reader schooled in psychological theory that it is just too simple to say that thought is the most basic or most fundamental function of the mind. This may seem simple, but its implications are extremely profound. All of the psychic entities that exist in other theories could be seen as themselves products of thought. They are someone's ideas about what forces drive people to behave in the wide variety of ways we label as the human experience. Hopefully, by the end of this book, the reader will start to consider that thought itself is the most powerful force in life, one that operates at both a surface level, and one that operates at a much more profound level; a level that is just now beginning to be more fully appreciated by the field.

Just as thought is the power that brings our physical sensations to life, so does thought animate our mental feelings, or emotions. All feelings are the product of thoughts. Some of those thoughts relate to the moment, and some are drawn from memory.

A feeling of fear, for example, is produced from the thought that I am about to be hit by a truck. I experience a feeling of distrust when I hear people talking and I have the thought that they were saying something quite different yesterday. Whatever is going on around us, we all process it via the vehicle of our thinking, using our capacity for analyzing, interpreting and giving meaning to that circumstance or event. All human emotions are direct products of our thoughts, of the meaning we think that situation holds for us.

Many psychologists hold the view that feelings are stored in memory from past experiences. This belief came about when they noticed that when something stimulates a memory, the feeling is reexperienced. In fact, when something stimulates a memory, it is the thought about that event that generates the feeling; the feeling to match the thought is born the moment we have the thought. If I have the thought, for example, that someone did something terrible to me in the past, I may interpret it in the frame of reference of thoughts like "How could someone possibly do something like that to another human being?" Given that thought I might feel anger, pain or self pity. If someone tells me that the other person at the time had been feeling depressed, overwhelmed by life and attacked or under some kind of threat to their well being, the way I look at what happened might change. I might see that the other person was just doing the best they could do, under the circumstances, to maintain their own well being. My feelings would then immediately change to feelings of compassion, forgiveness, or even regret that I responded so badly to them at the time.

Whatever my interpretation of the situation, at the time, my feelings will be completely consistent with that interpretation. Because our thoughts range widely along the positive/negative continuum, so do our emotions. Strangely enough, negative thoughts and the emotional reactions they provoke may have little to do with the situation at hand. Just as our thoughts enable us to imagine physical sensations into reality, so do our thoughts allow us to conjure worlds of emotions out of air.

For example, George may be peeling potatoes and a thought of his mother's habit of peeling potatoes while complaining about her husband crosses his mind. Suddenly, he is suffused with resentment at his father for distressing his mother, and at his mother for inflicting her misery on her young child. Distracted, George slices his thumb with the peeler, adding physical pain to the emotional landscape he is darkening with his mind. If George doesn't drop this chain of thought, his bad feelings will proliferate until they gel into a bad mood and ruin the rest of his day. And just who has created all this suffering? George innocently did it to himself with his thinking.

In another example, consider a couple who have wounded each other for years, building up plenty of mutual resentment in the process. At this point in their history together, an innocent remark by one spouse is all it takes to trigger negative memories. By taking these thoughts to heart, this unhappy pair continues to create feelings of anger or resentment that only contaminate their relationship further. On the other hand, if they can dismiss their negative thoughts and look at each other with clear eyes, they may feel a renewal of the love and tenderness that brought them together in the first place. Again, it is thought that shapes those feelings.

On a larger scale, social norms, cultural values, religious beliefs, political systems, and societal attitudes are created via thoughts. Thought has the power to create strong feelings and behaviors that result in wars, prejudice, starvation, oppression, and other social problems around the globe.

The Illusion That Feelings Are Primary

If it is thought that compels us to feel certain emotions, then why does it often seem as if the emotions came first? For example, we find ourselves feeling angry and only then start to think about what might be causing that rage. The fact is, we aren't aware of most of the thoughts that flow in an unending river through our brains. In addition, many of our habitual patterns of thinking are so entrenched that we don't notice we are thinking them and/or consider them to be absolute givens in the grand scheme of life.

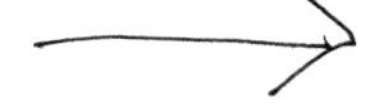

By the time we feel angry, then, an errant memory or belief has already taken hold. By the time this thought enters our consciousness, it has evolved into a feeling that is contaminating our natural good humor. Now we begin trying to figure out just what made us feel that way; we search for evidence to legitimize our bad feelings. What did my wife do this time to make me mad? What mischief are my kids up to? What is my boss trying to pull on me? The bad feeling, itself the by-product of an invisible, faster-than-light thought, leads us to new thoughts that are even further removed from the real source of our anger.

Here's an example. Whenever anybody says something negative to a person who was routinely criticized as a child, his knee-jerk reaction is self-pity and righteous indignation because he links any form of criticism with a lack of love from the significant adults in his life. If a teacher takes him to task for not completing a homework assignment, for example, he automatically has a rush of bad feelings and looks for a reason to blame the teacher for his own lack of preparation. The real source of his distress, of course, is a thought carried in his brain from the past.

People generally produce emotions and act in ways that are consistent with their outlook from moment to moment. Feelings are created in the moment by the thinker, and people can have very different thoughts and feelings about the same situation. For example, let's say a teacher is in a rotten mood and is coming down too hard on his students. One student is angry because this situation reminds her of the unfair pressure her parents exert on her. Another is mildly irritated because he feels he can't learn much in this climate. A third student finds the teacher's behavior amusing. A fourth is frustrated because he thinks the teacher doesn't appreciate all his hard work on the project at hand. The differences in these responses depend on how the students are conditioned to think about people in authority and on how they use their own thinking process.

While feelings, both positive and negative, can be extremely intense and compelling, they cannot be stored in memory and they do not shape the course and quality of our lives. Rather, it is the thought behind the feelings that is stored in memory, that creates our feelings moment to moment, and that determines what we make of our lives. It was an exciting insight for my colleagues and I when we realized that people are not irrevocable products of their past. The past may be immutable, but thoughts about the past are subject to change, which means we could offer our clients something practical and controllable, in the present.

The Key to Mental Health: Understanding Our Moment to Moment Thought Process

Early in our research, my colleagues and I realized that people vary greatly in their ability to distinguish between the content of their thoughts and the role the thought process plays in their lives. This continuum of understanding fascinated us as we began exploring the interrelationship between consciousness and thought. We found that people's ability to change their outlook, and the quality of their lives, varied directly in relation to their understanding of thought. We began to call this critical dimension of change "levels of understanding." We could see that this kind of understanding was different from an intellectual ability to grasp this model conceptually. In some people, it seemed that they had this understanding naturally, with no need, or even a real ability to conceptualize or to articulate it.

Some people take their opinions and ideas as the gospel while others realized that their ideas represent just one of many points of view. Some people are fascinated by different ideas while others feel threatened. Some people are compulsive about the "right" way to do things, while others are more easy-going and flexible. In addition, while many people share similar beliefs and values, they vary greatly in the degree to which they cling to their views as the one and only truth. For example, one political liberal can't abide anything or anyone conservative, while another could be open to some persuasion from the right.

After seeing positive results from applications of these principles over the last 12 years, my colleagues and I truly believe that ridding our clients of their emotional scars is a function of teach-

ing them to understand how they carry past traumas through time via thought—and that they have power over what thoughts they choose to entertain. The most important dimension of change, the one that had to come first, as a precursor to change in feelings, or behavior or lifestyle, was a rise in the person's level of understanding.

Emotional scars are etched in people's memories by how they interpret an event at the time it occurs. That interpretation is programmed into the brain as a memory, where it waits to be elicited by similar experiences. If our clients could grasp the role their thinking plays in maintaining that memory, we posited, then they could start to see past their habits of thinking and put the traumatic memory into perspective.

A few years ago, my colleagues and I received a federal grant to implement a county-wide training program for agencies working with high-risk, dysfunctional families in which many of the children had been battered or sexually abused. Previously, the agencies had led these children to believe that their hideous experiences had damaged them in irreversible ways. We showed the agencies a new approach.

By showing the children how they were using their thinking to carry their traumas close to the heart, they were able to wedge a distance between themselves and their terrible memories. They learned to keep the past from infecting the present without denying the horror that occurred. The improvement they showed—in their attitudes, their relationships with their parents, their schoolwork, and every other aspect of their lives—was remarkable.

Thought is the access switch to pain and pleasure. Anyone can relive a trauma at any time if he thinks about it in a certain frame of mind. In fact I was very successful at getting patients to do this during my clinical training. But if our clients learn how their thinking works—and thus how to nip their negative thoughts in the bud—then they are taking control of their lives, not reliving their traumas.

Trait or State? The Role Mood Plays in Personality

In the traditional psychoanalytic view, the human personality develops over time as a result of the id, ego, and super-ego resolving conflicts through various stages of psychosexual development. Given the complexity of this cumulative process, it is little wonder that traditional psychology sees personality traits as fixed and resistant to change. In this view, it also makes sense to associate certain emotional disorders with specific personality types.

Psychology of Mind has a different definition of personality. The paradigm posits that one component of people's make-up has to do with talents, aptitudes, and likes and dislikes—for music or painting, for sports and hobbies, for intellectual pursuits, and so on. Other facets of what the field of psychology now defines as personality include habitual mind-sets, moment-to-moment moods, and the way these two facets interact.

During the course of our research, we realized that if mental health is defined as an awareness of how we are using the thinking process, than we all experience different degrees of mental health depending on our current state of mind. In this model, state of mind is much more important than personality in the way it has been traditionally defined.

What I mean by state of mind is a result of combining a person's level of understanding of the role of their thinking and their mood. At the higher end of this scale, or continuum, is someone who realizes that their subjective reality is a result of their thinking and they are in a good mood. She is then more fully able to enjoy her good feelings and will worry less about losing this positive feeling state. In other words, she will be less likely to fear that something external will happen that could make her feel bad.

At the other end of this scale is someone who has no understanding that his thinking has anything to do with how life looks to him and he is in a bad mood. This state of mind will cause depression, hopelessness or fear. In this state of mind the per-

son feels that it really is his external circumstances, whatever they may be, that is causing his pain or suffering.

Changes in our moment to moment state of mind are what we normally call moods. In varying degrees throughout every day, we all feel up or down. When we are up, in a better mood, we use more common sense, feel good about ourselves, and experience insights on how to make our lives better. Similarly, all of us feel down, confused, frightened, upset, or overwhelmed by things at one time or another—and our thoughts follow suit. Most people's frame of mind is composed of more insecure, self-defeating thoughts when they are in negative states of mind.

My colleagues and I could see that people's basic aptitudes and preferences were fairly constant over time. Once you're good at numbers, you're always good at numbers. If you like going to the opera today, you'll probably like it 20 years from now, too. But the other side of personality—a person's mind-set—began to seem more like a temporary state shaped by mood than an immutable trait. People may think of themselves and be known as imaginative or stolid, easy-going or rigid, loving or cold, fun-loving or dutiful, but how much they actually exhibit these characteristics depends on their current state of mind or mood. For example, if "a good sport" is feeling good when she loses a tennis match, she is likely to show her usual grace. However, if she loses a match when she is feeling low, she may toss her racket and stomp off in a huff. Her basic personality doesn't change here, rather her mood does.

In this model a bad mood is essentially a more insecure frame of mind. It is a moment to moment shift in our level of mental health, a fluctuation around our current level of understanding. While it doesn't signal any real change in our basic personality, it impacts how we exhibit our personality traits, in either a more or less healthy direction.

In our observations and follow-up studies, we glimpsed how this dimension of personality was linked to state of mind. When people are in a good mood, they are more flexible, open-minded, and sensitive to others, adjusting their behavior and responses to the situation at hand. People in bad moods, however—states of mind where they felt insecure or threatened—tend to be rigid and uncompromising, sullen, hostile, anxious, or depressed.

Bad moods happen to all of us. They are so common that they don't appear to require reasons. The best way we found to help people navigate their low moods—to wait out the storm, as it were—was to teach them to discount their thoughts until their feelings were back on track, until they had rebounded into a state of mind that was more positive.

We began to teach our clients that emotions provide reliable clues to how we are functioning psychologically. Good feelings let us know that our thoughts are reliable and we are moving in the right direction. If we feel negative, hostile, or depressed, it's time to step back and relax, to suspend struggle and judgments. If we wait patiently, the common sense of wisdom will shine through the clouds and our thoughts will be trustworthy again.

Ego Generated Feelings Versus Unconditional Well Being

It can be difficult & confusing at times to learn to distinguish between positive feelings generated through what I would now call ego-gratification, versus feelings that come from our unconditional feelings of self worth and natural enjoyment of life. Ego generated positive feelings are more contingent and transitory in that they come from an accomplishment or victory that is associated with our learned self concept.

Self-concept and Insecurity

What people normally call self-concept or ego is nothing more than a bundled set of thoughts about our own personalities—who we are, what we are good at, and what we need to accomplish or possess in order to feel good about ourselves. Our self-concept isn't who we are, but who we think we are. It is also how we think we want or need other people to see us in order for us to feel good about ourselves.

The greatest threat to the self-image is insecurity, a catchall term for the fear that contaminates the thinking process. Insecurity exists in the form of, and contributes to the persistence of, habitual thinking patterns. Insecurity, first as a thought and then as a feeling, changes our mood and outlook for the worse. Most of the negative emotions we experience in life can be traced to the insecurity that rises when we think that something is threatening the way we have learned to think of ourselves.

Indeed, people routinely put their lives on the line to protect their image of themselves. Aging athletes keep struggling through the game, risking serious injury to keep their hot-shot self-images alive. Young gang members are ready to defend their turf to the death. Bulimic women do permanent harm to their health to maintain their (distorted) body image. Workaholics work themselves into ill health so they can keep thinking of themselves as top achievers. If we could observe ourselves more objectively, we would see that to one extent or another, all human beings pressure themselves to live up to standards they have imposed on themselves. When someone puts us down or we are threatened, we make ourselves feel that our very survival is at stake.

Most of us can allow ourselves to feel good temporarily when we accomplish something we feel is important to our self image. For example, when we beat someone at golf or tennis, when we do well on an exam, when we get praise for hard work from our boss and so-on. Yet these feelings are very conditional and are not a source of true self worth or contentment. In fact, it is always stressful to try to live up to our own learned standards.

Suppose I see myself as a generous, caring person. When I am not in a good mood, I might not be as generous or caring as I feel I should be. I will then feel guilty and get down on myself. These feelings will limit my understanding so that I can't see that it is only my thinking that is bringing me down. Another example, suppose I base my self worth on being appreciated by my boss. What if he gets upset about something and is critical or angry at me? My self worth is out the window.

It makes no difference that the self-image we are so quick to defend includes qualities we'd all like to have. Even a positive self-concept can get us into trouble because when we take it seriously, we lose our ability to keep things in perspective. If my self image is based on my ability to get straight A grades in school, I may feel insecure and depressed if I get an A- on a test. If I think I am popular, I may feel badly, and get insecure if one person doesn't act as if they like me, or are distracted by something else and don't pay attention to me in the way I want.

These beliefs about ourselves that we hold so dear are nothing more than learned habits of thought. The amount of suffering we experience when these beliefs are threatened correlates exactly with how attached we are to our thinking. If people are in an insecure state of mind where they identify with their own self-image, they feel negative emotions whenever they perceive a threat to that image.

They also tend to take personally events that have nothing to do with them. For example, if my self-image is tied to my strength in weight-lifting, I feel jealous of people who can pump more iron or have better physiques. I feel secure only around people who are weaker than me. The same concept holds true for people who base their well-being on how smart or popular or attractive they are. They will always feel some insecurity based on how they judge themselves against others—and how they perceive others to be judging them.

Separate Realities and Personality

Because we all learn to think differently, no two people see things in the same way. If we all looked honestly at this fact, we would recognize that not one of our friends sees things in exactly the same way that we see things. Even our closest friends have serious differences of opinion with us. At times we have misunderstandings and conflicts with the people who care the most for us. This occurs because we are innocently interpreting things differently, or have different expectations and different priorities, or we each hold different things about our relationship as being most important to our self esteem.

At lower levels of understanding of the role of thought, it is easy to take these differences personally. We don't see them as conditioned thinking but rather as something to fight about, change, or fix. The majority of us have come to feel that our way of thinking is right and everyone else's is wrong if it is too different from ours. We tend to act like an Archie Bunker, in our own way, because other people are threatening our reality—at least that's the way it seems. The more someone looks different, acts different or feels that things we think are important are just not that important to them, the more we judge their reality and the more vociferously we defend our own reality.

The ways that people tend to become attached to their separate reality tends to reinforce and perpetuate insecurity. Insecurity is the bane of sound mental functioning. When separate realities are taken seriously, insecurity is hard at work. We become obsessed with defending our version of reality. Our negative thoughts take on a more compelling sense of urgency—they seem very "real" indeed. When people buy into thoughts born of insecurity, and feel an urgency about defending their separate reality, the result is a chronic bad mood—which in turn creates a lowered level of awareness that they are operating at the effect of their own conditioned thinking.

A New Model for Mental Health

As we observed how insecurity consistently contaminated our clients' sense of well-being, my colleagues and I started to make some links of logic. It was clear that good moods go hand in hand with a higher awareness of the thought process and less attachment to the content of one's thoughts. Conversely, a high level of insecurity—feelings that our self-image is at stake—produces negative thoughts. Taken seriously, these thoughts lead to negative feelings that lead to low moods. These negative states of mind are accompanied by less awareness of the thinking process and greater attachment to the content of thought. In more insecure states of mind, then, our thinking, emotions, and behaviors would seem more compelling, more out of our control.

Most of traditional psychology posits that many emotional disorders are personality disorders. Yet the mood swings people experience from moment to moment have little to do with personality and everything to do with insecurity. Rather than being linked to fixed personality traits, states of mental health are really states of mind that change constantly for all of us depending on how much insecurity is present in our lives. Truly, insecurity was the new, and we would say a more accurate, practical barometer of mental health.

My colleagues and I were very excited by the implications of this notion. What would happen if people could recognize that they experience different levels of mental health from moment to moment? What if a woman started to lash out at her husband and suddenly noticed that her feeling was produced by her mood—her insecure state of mind—and not by him? Could she see the link between her thoughts and emotions sufficiently to change her behavior?

When we put this hypothesis to the test, we found the answer to be "yes." People could indeed connect their moods with their thinking in a way that changed their behavior. A four-year pilot program with extremely high-risk families in Miami public housing projects provided us with dramatic proof that our theories held water. At the beginning of the program, most of our clients were either physically or emotionally abusing their children. Most of these parents had themselves been abused or neglected as children and had sworn not to repeat the pattern with their own children. Yet they couldn't seem to find a way out of this trap until they recognized the link between their learned ways of thinking and how they responded to their own children.

After the three months of parent training, most of the parents in the program came to understand that their moods were a reaction to their own thinking—and that their thinking would only make matters worse until they felt better. The parents learned not to interact with their children when they were upset, but to take a break and cool down until they could listen and respond in a more helpful way. They learned to wait until they felt more loving and saw the innocence of their children. As a result, their relationships with their children improved immediately and significantly. A six year follow-up study with these families is now showing that most of these changes have been sustained over time.

Thought and Habits

Habits develop when people program a thought into their memory systems and call it up every time a certain stimulus appears. Many habits are incredibly useful, of course; imagine what a bother it would be to have to learn to tie your shoelaces anew every time you put on your shoes. Those habits that arise through the stimulus of insecurity, though, can wreck havoc in our lives. When some people feel insecure, they light a cigarette. Others pour a Scotch and water. Others shoot up heroin or smoke crack. Others overeat. Others beat their wives or flirt with other people's wives. Others may pick a fight. Others may retreat into sullen withdrawal. The common denominator across all these self destructive habits is that each is what the person has learned to do, or feel is the best they can do, when they are caught in the grip of insecurity.

Coping Versus Mental Health

What most researchers in the mental health field normally look at as symptoms of dysfunction I would now say are really the coping styles people develop. People develop these coping styles to minimize the amount of suffering they produce when they are thinking negative or insecure thoughts. If people do not understand that their thinking has anything to do with their suffering, they will attempt to do the best they can to manipulate the external environment to gain a better feeling.

This manipulation could include hitting their spouse or children, picking a fight with someone, cheating, stealing or otherwise trying to gain more control of their situation any way they can, or it could include drinking and using drugs. It could include self pity as an attempt to feel better or obtain sympathy. It could include violence or lashing out verbally at others. It could include escaping into an inner world through delusional states or hallucinations. All of these things could be viewed as coping mechanisms, the best that occurs to people to do to minimize their pain when they do not know about thought, and how it is working in their day to day lives.

If people can recognize these patterns as habits of thought and realize that their insecurity is speaking, they can begin to free themselves from destructive patterns and begin to develop more positive and useful patterns. The parents in Miami, for example, learned to walk away when they were so upset they wanted to knock their children across the room. They then cultivated the habit of sitting down, sharing their ideas and concerns with their children, and listening to what the kids had to say. As they saw the wonderful effect these new patterns had on their relationship with their children, they realized that the world really could change for the better, and they felt the stirring of hope and possibility.

While something as ephemeral as a thought is always a root cause of psychological distress, we also recognize that the depression and fear that thoughts produce are very painful feelings. If people's thinking creates emotions such as hopelessness or disillusionment, these feelings have tremendous impact when people see them as "real." And as long as a negative mindset holds sway, any attempt to improve the situation is doomed to failure, which further "proves" that things will never work out and blackens an already negative perspective.

Our depressed and phobic patients are truly suffering. Our role as professionals is to help alleviate that suffering. If suffering stems from the inability to notice when habits of thinking have you in their clutches, it is only logical that our job as therapists is to teach people about the thinking process to help them unlearn their habits. By realizing that these habits are thoughts, a person can often change the thinking patterns of a lifetime and erase the effects of the past.

In fact, my colleagues and I saw immediate and significant change in people's behavior when they gained enough perspective to recognize the consequences of their learned habits of thought. A positive frame of reference enables us to see the world more objectively and frees our natural intelligence to do its work. A higher perspective may allow a boss to see she has been so quick to judge employees' performance that they are too nervous to perform very well. It may suddenly become obvious to a husband that his wife isn't deliberately trying to drive him crazy, but is merely doing things the way she has always done them. It may strike someone on welfare that he has been hobbled by habitual thoughts that he couldn't do any better, and that it is within his power to change that way of thinking. And so on.

By stepping outside the thought-feeling-behavior cycle, people can see past despair and disillusionment to more hopeful feelings, which in turn provides fuel for positive change. Our clinical experience and our demonstration programs in prevention and early intervention have drawn us to conclude that people are able to give up their attachment to coping once they understand this cycle, and as they begin to reexperience the unconditional good feelings that come when they let go of old habits of insecure thinking.

In the following chapters, I will further explain the relationships among thought, consciousness, and innate intelligence that have given rise to the kind of positive results we saw in pilot programs in Miami, Hawaii, California, Minnesota, and New York. And I will explore the implications of these relationships for new models of psychotherapy, prevention, and community development.

CHAPTER FOUR

The Path to Positive Change

In graduate school, I learned to think of change as something that required struggle—for both the therapist and the client. But when we looked at long-term studies with children, we noticed that young people change their outlook continually and effortlessly as they grow. If you think back to how you saw things as a child, as an adolescent, and finally as an adult, you would probably agree that your perspective changed dramatically at every stage. This process is called maturation, and it's the most natural thing in the world.

Maturation doesn't automatically stop at age 21. In fact it continues automatically when we understand how thoughts create our experience of life. The more we realize this fact, the less seriously we take our habits of thought and the more we continue to evolve so that we see the world from a broader, wiser perspective. From this perspective, we have insights that resolve things that troubled or overwhelmed us in the past, because we learn from life. This is what the capacity we are calling common sense is; the innate ability to learn from experience.

All of us are inherently able to grow in understanding throughout life, because that's the way the human mind is designed. Just because we have the capacity for growth doesn't mean that we are always changing for the better. In trying to identify those factors that facilitate the maturation process versus those that impede it, we noticed in our clients that the quality of their feelings seemed to be one important catalyst for positive change.

A number of studies across large samples have shown that children learn and mature most rapidly in loving and accepting environments where they feel secure. Children who are emotionally deprived or grow up in hostile environments tend to retreat into insecure, defensive, and rebellious patterns of behavior that match their feelings. They do not trust adults and have a harder time in school. They are more rigid and biased in their habits and attitudes.

How do we link these observations back into our assertion that thought is the key variable determining anyone's state of mind? Since these youth have grown up in homes where there is a prevalence of insecure, rigid or hostile thinking around them, they learn to think in insecure ways themselves. They function, in their day to day lives, with an insecure belief system. As stated in the previous chapter, an insecure belief system creates negative feelings. As these children move into more nurturing environments, however, they begin to open up. Study after study reveals that when young people feel secure and fully accepted, they are fascinated with everything about life, eager to learn and master new things. They are able to thrive on and enjoy their experiences from moment to moment. Their natural, innate resiliency resurfaces.

At times, haven't we all wished that we could be as carefree and enthusiastic as children? Perhaps the most exciting thing our research is revealing is that the child-like feelings of wonder, curiosity, gratitude, and joy are available to all adults, too—and that those feelings sow the seeds of learning, motivation, and happiness. Over and over again, we have seen in our clients that positive feelings are what grease the wheels of change—and that once those feelings are present, change comes more easily.

The real question is then how do we get back into the flow of life in a way that reengages the natural process of maturation leading to continuous learning and change? In the last chapter we introduced the concept of separate realities. As soon as someone gets stuck in a separate reality in a way that causes feelings of insecurity, they will, either consciously or unconsciously, impede their own growth and change. They will put their energy into defending and maintaining their separate reality. Especially if they think their survival depends on it, all their attention will get locked up in defending what they already believe. Obviously this focus will stop most new learning and insight.

However, when someone realizes how thought works, what separate realities do to us, and how the flow of original, creative and insightful thinking is set back in motion, that person is back on track. She will begin to have new ideas and insights every day and continue to learn and grow for the rest of her life. This type of realization leads to what we have defined as a higher level of understanding.

Levels of Understanding

Psychology of Mind defines "levels of understanding" as the degree to which we recognize the role thought plays in our lives. For example, our level of understanding rises when we learn to distinguish between conditioned and original thought. Our understanding rises another notch when we can view our emotions as feedback, unerringly alerting us to the quality of our thinking. We also function at a higher level of understanding when we grasp the link between self-concept and insecurity. Our understanding also rises when we recognize that we have access to secure, positive feelings within ourselves that have nothing to do with our conditioning, or with our circumstances.

When we have a limited level of understanding of how the thought process works, conditioned habits of thought seem real. These insecure thoughts then invariably lead to negative emotions and dysfunctional behavior patterns. At higher levels of understanding, positive, secure feelings engage our innate capacity for wisdom and self-esteem—and negative thoughts have less pull. Our moment to moment level of understanding corresponds with just how conscious we are of our current state of mind and how it is shaped by our thoughts.

In the Psychology of Mind paradigm, the antithesis of understanding—and the source of negative states of mind—is insecurity. At low levels of understanding, we can't tell the difference between what is actually happening and what we are thinking about it.

For example, if a young person grows up with argumentative parents who take their bad moods out on him, he may mistakenly assume that other people's problems are always his fault. His self-concept may be based on his belief that he is the kind of person who always screws things up for other people. This habit of thinking is a direct path to insecurity. He may act withdrawn and feel like an undesirable person. He may get anxious and make bad decisions due to his anxiety level.

If he understands that his reaction is nothing more than a habit, though, the insecurity disappears. He will see the link between his thoughts and the way things seem to turn out in his life. Mental health is our default position. As soon as insecurity drains away, it is replaced automatically with positive feelings that avert us away from problems toward solutions and growth. First he may realize that he is not always the cause of others difficulties. He may then see how he can make a contribution to the lives of those around him. He is on the way to a continuous evolution of his wisdom and maturity.

It is impossible to force people to change the way they think and behave. All we can do is help them to realize that they have a choice by helping them to raise their level of understanding. Change then again becomes more natural and self propelled. Continuous change is fueled by new insights that come naturally when we are not stuck in a fixed frame of reference.

A New Perspective on Change

I once had a client whose boss was so impatient and threatening that she was nearly paralyzed by intimidation. After she received some counseling, it hit her that her boss behaved as he did because he felt insecure. He knew his employees didn't like him and felt he needed to crack the whip even harder because of it.

From her new perspective of compassion, she could see his blind spots, which kept her from taking his behavior personally. When he yelled at her, she was able to hear him out and try to be helpful rather than react defensively. Before long, he was asking her for advice and assistance. When other staff members quizzed her on how she had calmed him down, she could only say that she understood him better now. Her new perspective felt so natural to her that she had trouble explaining how the shift had occurred.

In another instance, we worked with an experienced counselor of young gang members during a recent therapist training program. He was great at building rapport with his kids and handling crises because he had grown up in similar circumstances and could connect with their reality. He was less successful in getting the kids to see the value of school. He had tried many behavior modification techniques and reward systems to get them to change their self-image vis-a-vis school, but nothing seemed to work.

After a week of training with us, the counselor decided to try teaching his kids what he had learned about how their thinking worked. He became less interested in changing them and accepted them the way they were, confident in their inner resources for change. From this stance, he engaged them in discussions about thought. He asked them to describe what kind of thoughts might lead kids to drop out or lead a dangerous life—then let them draw their own conclusions.

The result? The kids changed. Within two weeks, three of them had returned to school and within a month, three more had dropped out of their gangs and gone back to school. The counselor said he didn't know what he was doing that was so different—except that he saw the possibility that they could change just by understanding their own thinking. He also recognized that he trusted their natural capacity for common sense and for recognizing what was in their own best interests. He realized he didn't have to beat them over the head to get them interested in school.

These stories are typical of many of the people my colleagues and I have counseled. The kind of change they create for themselves has nothing to do with the intellect, will power, or "behavior modification." Rather, it is the result of a shift in perspective that enables people to glimpse the relationship between thought and consciousness and thereby liberate their inner intelligence, the source of insight and growth.

Beliefs Limit Perspective

Every human being has a belief system that's made up of all the beliefs and values we accumulate throughout our lives. In graduate school, as my colleagues and I studied how innovations in any field tended to evolve into accepted practice, we noticed that new ideas invariably met resistance from those practitioners who were wedded to previous ways of plying their trade. These people were very intelligent, but they had such strong belief systems that they could not envision the relevance of the new ideas to their work.

The same phenomenon seems to apply to personal change. People who become stuck in a fixed frame of reference or belief system cannot see the relevance of any other outlook on life. Literally everything they experience is interpreted through the logic of their existing beliefs and therefore looks just the way they thought it would.

Let's say a woman has learned to doubt her ability to make friends. Ever since she was a child, she has felt ill at ease with others because she figures they won't like her. And in fact, they usually aren't drawn to her because she seems so aloof, which only goes to reinforce her beliefs about herself. Any effort she makes to change this pattern will be doomed until she can drop her beliefs about herself. Until then, she will always feel awkward and uncomfortable, a stance that others interpret as aloofness or introversion.

When we try to use our beliefs to drive change, we are triggering a self-validating and self-defeating framework of logic that stands in the way of progress. If we hope to blast through the status quo maintained by the intellect, we must shift to a vantage point where we can recognize that this self-defeating cycle of beliefs exists only through the power of our own thinking.

To say the same thing a different way, relying on what we "know" to think our way toward change is a fruitless task. Change is the product of insight, and insight is the product not of the intellect but of our inborn intelligence. This source of wisdom or maturity is available to all; gaining access to it hinges on our consciousness of our thoughts and of ourselves as the thinkers. Gaining this knowledge, again is what we would call a higher level of understanding.

Having the courage to let go of insecurity-generated thoughts without trying to replace them with other beliefs enables us to engage the natural capacity for insight and learning immediately. In other words, "empty-headed" is actually a desirable way to be at times!

It can be hard for people to move into a state of not knowing—of ambiguity and openness—because the ego always wants to stay on top of things. In this model of human nature, the ego is seen as a self image that is held in place by insecurity. In other words, the ego is an image of ourselves that we take seriously, that we use to make ourselves feel important. Thus the ego wants to hang onto and make important what we already know as a way of bolstering our self image.

At lower levels of understanding, we feel insecure not knowing how to prove ourselves or live up to our self-images. However, letting go of knowing what we need to be happy can move us into a new reality where we don't have to prove a thing in order to enjoy self-confidence and peace of mind.

Ego Creates Barriers to Change

Self-concept—or our beliefs about who we are, what we like and don't like, and what we need to feel good about ourselves—is a subset of the belief system. As we discussed in Chapter 3, the importance we give our fixed ideas about ourselves (which depends on how much insecurity we're feeling) is the source of most emotional ups and downs. Think of the way rocks divert the flow of a river and roil the waters. Similarly, when insecurity enters our lives, it blocks the flow of positive feelings and thus limits our ability to move forward. The ego and insecurity are two sides of the same coin. We always have one coming along with the other, they are inseparable.

My colleagues and I used to hold that change could come only as the product of a "healthy ego," so we drilled our clients on techniques for building their self-images. Over time, we confirmed that when people attach their feelings of self-worth to thinking of themselves in certain ways and insecurity enters the picture, they go into a defensive mode and become highly resistant to change. In other words, we saw in our clients that a strong ego not only doesn't facilitate growth; it actually blocks it.

For example, at one time we would have helped a client feel proud that he is assertive, a real doer in the world. When he feels insecure around people he wants to impress, though, he will most likely exaggerate these qualities and come off as pushy, aggressive, or arrogant. If people respond negatively to him, he may get defensive and even more aggressive, because he has attached his self-esteem to the concept he has of himself. He believes he has no choice but to keep proving himself in order to keep his ego pumped; he doesn't see that other options exist.

The ego is perhaps the single greatest barrier to change, and it can get us in all kinds of trouble. A child who thinks of herself as funny may cut up inappropriately in class when she feels insecure. She thinks she is proving her comedic talents, while other students see her as loud or stupid. The captain of the football team may start to talk down to his friends and put on airs in a way he thinks is expected of him, but this behavior may cause him to lose his friends—and lose the focus that made him such a good player in the first place.

We found it helps to show clients the difference between self-concept (ego) and genuine self-esteem. Genuine, unconditional self esteem occurs naturally when people find peace of mind that is not contingent on fortifying their beliefs about themselves. They are then able to maintain their good feelings in any situation, under most circumstances. In this state of mind they can use their wisdom to respond appropriately to different situations and they more easily grasp and have empathy for others' frames of references. Genuine self-esteem is the same as self respect. Once we accept and respect ourselves completely, we can then truly respect and have empathy for others.

For example, in our programs in public housing, many of the mothers stayed in abusive relationships because they couldn't picture themselves without a man in their lives—even a man who was abusing them and their children. As these women learned to let go of this belief, they told their mates they had to change or leave.

As these women began to feel better, they either found new partners or the quality of their relationships improved as their old partners began to respect them more. At the same time, the men realized that they didn't have to perpetually prove their manhood in the relationship. Deeper feelings of true caring accompanied these changes, replacing the need for inappropriate physical gratification or control.

The need to maintain any self-concept limits us to judging what is going on this minute by the yardstick of past experience. These preconceptions keep us from seeing or learning anything new.

A New Approach to Therapy

With our clients as our teachers and ego-created resistance as an example, it became clear that we had thought change was arduous because our old methods for helping people immobilized people in the status quo or actually made matters worse. For example, teaching people problem-solving skills makes them feel they need to solve all their problems before they can be happy. Assertiveness training has a similar result: people feel they need to call others on the errors of their ways before they can feel good about themselves.

The most pervasive technique of all, perhaps, is having people explore the past. By having them delve into negative memories, we were helping them to re-experience the thoughts that made them feel insecure in the first place. By helping clients to explore their negative feelings, we got them into states of mind where they were too disturbed to experience insights or let their inborn "native" intelligence show them a more direct path to genuine and effortless self-esteem.

Our clients were showing us that positive change has more to do with releasing something we already have rather than adding something we lack. It has to do with banishing insecurity so that our natural positive feelings can flow freely. It has to do with breaking the attachment to ego and ingrained beliefs, not building it up. And we noticed that when our clients are able to tap into their unconditional self-esteem, they automatically exhibit the attributes we had been trying to teach—like problem-solving acumen and assertiveness, when these behaviors are appropriate. They also regained their natural joyful feelings and fascination with life, producing an eager optimism that helps them move forward in life.

Viewing Change as Impersonal

My colleagues and I observed that clients changed fastest when they distanced their insights from themselves and applied them to all human beings. We remembered from our own school days our thirst to understand the broad principles that made psychology a science and not just an amalgam of conjectures about human functioning. We wanted to help our clients see the value of setting their own experiences, thoughts, and feelings in the context of universal principles of mental health. We decided to create a warm, stimulating learning climate in therapy—as well as a more collegial relationship with our clients—so we could work together to learn more about the links between mental health, thought, and consciousness. We found that this goal was helped by helping them take their situation less personally and by disconnecting the idea of changing from trying to prove themselves or feel more worthwhile. We found that one of the stimulants to change was becoming happier the way they were.

In case after case in our research, my colleagues and I found that when people are in a good mood, they learn easily via an enhanced capacity for insight and they are more receptive to change. They feel less compelled to defend their ingrained beliefs about themselves and take things personally. They can see that they are the ones creating their thoughts and thus are open to other perspectives on the world. They don't have to confront past memories or work through negative feelings to arrive at healthier states of mind. Feeling positive and serene is clearly a solvent that clears the way for insights that enable our clients to solve or dismiss their problems.

Our clients' levels of understanding increased the most when we taught them about thought in a light-hearted atmosphere. We saw the importance of rapport in showing clients that we liked and respected them the way they were, and we avoided pointing out negative habits of thought until we achieved sufficient rapport so they could listen without getting defensive. We began to look for health in our clients rather than pathology. This was a profound change in itself. We learned to show empathy without commiserating with clients' negative perceptions, for commiseration made negative thinking seem more "real." And we learned not to react to clients' expressions of self-concept, either positive or negative.

We found that people raised their level of understanding fastest when they found contentment first. Rather than trying harder to prove themselves, people learned to drop their grip on insecure thoughts. When they did this they found that they had less on their mind. When they had less on their mind they automatically had access to quieter, more serene states of mind. This quieter state of mind was not produced by any technique for meditation, but occurred naturally when they made insecure thoughts less important to feelings of self worth.

A quieter mind led to reflection rather than reactive thinking. When people could see that their habits of thought produced their insecure outlook, they calmed down. When they calmed down, they had insights about thought and ways to improve their lives. These insights enabled them to calm down even more and find deeper positive feelings. It was a positive cycle that began with either a non-contingent positive feeling or a realization about the function of thought in life.

It helped clients to realize that there was nothing they had to do in therapy beyond grasping the logic of the principles of mind, thought, and consciousness. It helped to realize that quieter, positive feelings came automatically from understanding, as did insights. It also helped to know that taking our thoughts less seriously helped to evoke wisdom. We suggested to clients that rather than grapple with their problems, they could enjoy their lives more. They were helped by knowing that they possessed a natural, internal source of good feelings; that not all the good feelings stemmed from their habits (e.g., getting drunk, fighting, avoiding challenges). We reinforced the notion that original, creative thoughts facilitated change faster than upset, angry, or disturbing ones.

Taken together, these observations helped clients see change as easier and more natural. Pointing clients in this direction helped unstick them from the freeze-frame world of self-concept. The natural maturation process accelerated as people were less tempted to get stuck in habitual patterns of thought—even new ones. Positive change became a continuous pattern for most clients.

In the next chapters, I will explore the implications of this new understanding of change on psychotherapy. I will discuss the impact of the "health of the helper" on the success of the therapeutic process, and the role therapists play in teaching people about their own capacity for mental health. I will also explore the approaches that seem to elicit the best outcomes.

CHAPTER FIVE

Health of the Helper: The Foundation of Effective Therapy

The depth of understanding of their own capacity for health is one of the best tools therapists have. The health of the helper is a catalyst for clients realizing their own capacity for a healthy outlook. The kind of understanding that helps people change for the better, in this approach, comes in the form of insights or realizations.

I'm not talking about the kind of insight which involves remembering traumatic incidents from the past and then linking them with our current hang-ups. Rather, the insights that occur to people in this form of therapy reveal how we create our present experience of life moment to moment. We do this using our thinking capacity, including how we hold our memories of the past.

In this model, traumas or incidents from our past are recreated and given the appearance of reality now via the conditioned thinking process. Insights about the role of thought make this process more and more obvious. People can take responsibility for overcoming their past when they realize how it is carried through time, and hold their thoughts differently. As we understand more about how this thought process works, we are able to change our mind; the thought process become more understandable and more manageable.

Teaching clients about the thought process and the wisdom available from their innate intelligence—the very heart of this form of therapy—is the catalyst for insights that set the change process in motion. We found in practice that, most often, clients were inspired to genuine insights via the insights of their therapists. The quality and frequency of therapists' insights is a function of their personal depth of understanding. It is not the intention of this book to go into a great deal of depth regarding the therapy protocols or modalities that have developed over the last fifteen years of applying this approach. In Chapter Six, I give a broad overview of the phases or elements that seem critical to Health Realization therapy generally. An entire book could be, and surely will be, written on this topic alone. Yet whatever the therapists do, a critical catalyst in the process is the helper's depth of personal understanding and their mental well being.

The Understanding of the Helper

When we researched how positive change in therapists affected their work with clients, we found a direct positive relationship between therapists' progress in applying this understanding of mental health to their lives and the progress their clients made. As a result, it became clear to us that the best preparation for counseling others is to deepen our own grasp of these principles. Over and over again, we have seen that as insights enhance our students' lives, they automatically become better helpers.

It is logical that when, as therapists, we more deeply experience our own mental health, the more real and natural it becomes for us. The more real it is to us, the more easily we can explain it to others and help them to engage their own core of health. Time and again, my colleagues and I have found that the health of the helper makes the biggest difference in successful Psychology of Mind counseling. What I mean here by the health of the helper is the depth and clarity of their realizations concerning how their own thinking generates their experience of life.

Learning to live more of the time in a state of unconditional well-being is a wonderful benefit in and of itself. When it is also the key to professional effectiveness, a therapist has the best of both worlds. Many of our students reported that they initially felt that they couldn't be happy themselves when their clients suffered so much. With so much suffering in the world, they felt that it was almost irresponsible to concern themselves with their own happiness. Most of these students began feeling excited when they recognized that their foremost qualification to teach Psychology of Mind was their own happiness.

They were delighted when they made the connection; to realize that their peace of mind is what helps them to access their innate intelligence in a way that helps clients get in touch with their own wisdom, too. Again, I want to repeat the disclaimer that this step is not sufficient to enable a therapist to provide therapy using the Health Realization model. Yet it is a necessary element of the process. In the following sections of this chapter, I will attempt to delineate the ways in which it helps.

Providing a Therapeutic Milieu

It is safe to say that people who come to therapists for help are feeling insecure, overwhelmed, hopeless, or hostile. If the therapist is genuinely secure, hopeful, and positive—and can pretty much stay that way irrespective of the client's state of mind or behavior—the client is more likely to calm down and feel better. This relationship holds true particularly when the helper is able to stay compassionate and reassuring. This is easier when we trust the clients innate capacity for health. It is then easier to avoid either becoming patronizing or seeming insensitive to the clients suffering. The therapist's depth of understanding is what enables this balance to be maintained. When therapists are able to maintain their well being, to show genuine empathy toward every client, and to trust the clients health, they also model mental health for clients in a way that hits home.

How Understanding Helps Teaching

In both our clinical and community research settings, my colleagues and I have observed a link between the helper's level of mental health and how well they could intuit what their clients needed to learn. They were better equipped to discern how their clients' lives looked through their clients' filters of thought. They more quickly noticed what their clients most basic beliefs were, beliefs that the client himself may not have recognized because they had become so habitual as a way of viewing life. As our students gained self-assurance, their mental clarity increased. The clearer and stronger the students became, the less intellectual baggage—predispositions and judgments—they brought to counseling. They were also better able to see how to make what they were teaching relevant, breaking it down so that it was more obvious and interesting to each client, so that it touched their day to day experience, putting things in a new light.

One of the most successful of our programs was a federally funded grant to train parents living in high risk communities to teach parenting classes and to work with other parents who were having problems with drugs, poverty, child neglect and abuse. The parents who were chosen were those who had benefited most themselves from a series of parenting classes and resident self-esteem groups carried out under another federally funded delinquency prevention grant. An independent evaluation done of the program showed that the parents who were most successful in counseling or teaching other parents what they had learned, were those who had benefited the most themselves.

For example, these parents were able to teach other parents how to improve the quality of their interactions with their children, even when they were upset or feeling bad themselves. They were able to teach the logic of walking away and calming down before they interacted with their children, because they saw so clearly the extent to which this understanding had improved their relationships with their own children. No matter what the child had done, they were not tempted to tell other parents that they should lay into them. They showed them by example how not to react with physical or mental abuse.

In general, as our students recognized the role thinking played in their own ups and downs, they were less likely to be thrown off-track by their clients' problems. They were less inclined to see their clients' illness or pathology as primary and more inclined to see health. And as they recognize that everyone has access to healthy functioning, they are more hopeful about their clients' progress and prospects for success—and better able to maintain a positive, respectful therapeutic climate.

The Link Between Seeing and Realizing Health

Once we awaken our own inner capacity for health, we automatically respect this same capacity in our clients. Rather than seeing clients as subordinates in need of teaching, we see them as equals who may at times even have something to teach us. We know that they can change their outlook in a moment via an insight that takes them beyond their own thinking. We can appreciate—and learn from—the insights they express as they begin tapping into their real capacity for health.

The more profound a therapist's understanding of these health realization principles, the easier it is to work from a state of service. In a state of service, our only agenda is our clients' best interests. The prerequisite for this attitude is the helper's humility, which in turn stems from his ability to still the ego's need to prove itself. Humility means we want to contribute whether or not we get credit for our effort. We don't need to be right; we just want to make a difference. In a state of service, we see the world from a broader perspective because our well-being is not attached to the situation. This enables us to keep our sense of humor and see what is best for our clients. In this state of mind, we can help people find their self-confidence merely by how we approach and engage them. They can feel our respect because it is real. And they can feel that we care about them, because we do.

Building Relationships in the Moment

When my colleagues and I first started our parenting and family counseling programs in public housing, we went out of our way to show people that we felt they were already doing their best to be good parents. If helpers can truly believe that everyone is doing the best they can under the circumstances, they can be compassionate and respectful. In this particular program, that was the only way we could gain our clients' trust and sustain their interest. We had to be able to see their capacity for health and their innocence, regardless of how they were then living their lives.

In addition, in order to create a relaxed, positive environment where people would open themselves to learning, we had to maintain our own well-being in situations that were usually chaotic and sometimes violent. If we had not genuinely seen people as healthy and shown respect for them and their capacity for health, the program would never have gained a foothold in the community, much less produced any positive results.

We also had to maintain our well-being in order to stay flexible and resourceful in the face of emergencies. If, for example, a shooting had occurred the night before and everyone in the community was up in arms, we had to be able to cancel our classes and hang out on the stoops, the playground, and the parking lot, helping the residents deal with their feelings and reactions.

Teaching Health in "Real" Time

Effective therapy is not a cookbook process and we cannot control how people will respond to our efforts. We have to learn to teach what is needed at the time it is needed. That's where the therapists' insights come into play. Being able to deliver meaningful, helpful insights requires keeping the principles of mind, thought, and consciousness as the framework for our lives and our work, every moment of the day. Then, rather than trying to teach specific subjects in a specific order, we can draw on our own understanding to see what each individual needs in the moment.

Knowing How and When to Teach

When our clients are caught up in their problems, we cannot blithely tell them that their despair is no more than a thought. We have to be able to listen for understanding and respond with something nonthreatening that hits them where they live. We have to inspire in them a genuine hope that things can get better. We want to avoid teaching in a way that makes people more defensive or resistant, guilty or ashamed. These feeling states are all impediments to learning and to change.

We once had a client who was a teenager in a class for severely emotionally disturbed youth. He had been in this special program for almost five years. When he was referred to us, his mother stated that he hated therapists and had refused to go back to any other psychologist he had seen. When the young man came in we spent the first session getting to know him, finding out about his interests and his views of why school and interpersonal relations with adults were hard for him. We found out that he liked rock and roll, and had been trying to start his own band. He was surprised that we could talk knowledgeably and were genuinely interested in things in which he was interested.

His therapist could see that he mistrusted adults generally and thought that everyone was out to get him. The therapist engaged him as a normal teenager, talked about music, girls, his problems with his parents and listened to how he was viewing school and his problems there. They talked about movies, television and other non-charged things, had a few laughs and the therapist asked him if it was important to him to not be seen or labeled as emotionally disturbed.

His mother called prior to the next session saying that he was eager to return, expressing astonishment that he had reminded her not to forget to pick him up early at school for his next appointment. He said he liked coming in because the people there treated him as normal. When he had gained a solid rapport with his therapist, they talked about why he thought he was in a special classroom for disturbed youth. Since he thought all adults were against him, he at first blamed his teacher and the principal for plotting against him, not liking him and going out of their way to make his life miserable.

His mother felt that rock and roll and TV were both tools of the devil. The father was rigid and obsessive and had verbally abused him prior to the parents' divorce. The father still thought the school was coddling him and should be administering even more stringent punishment. He had never had success in communicating or feeling understood by adults.

As the therapist listened to his view of the world, she was able to show him that not all adults were the same. She revealed that she knew his teacher, that she liked him and probably would love to see him get back into a normal classroom. As he calmed down and trusted more his own common sense, he was able to recognize how the things he did in reaction to his thoughts made his life harder. Picking fights, throwing desks around and swearing at his teacher, he realized, made it harder for her to help him with what he said he wanted, to be treated as normal. He started to see cause and effect differently in relation to his own behavior and how people responded to him.

He approached his teacher and made a contract with her concerning how his behavior would have to change if she would consider that he could eventually function appropriately in a normal classroom. She stated that she was amazed at how cooperative and mature he had become. By that next semester she was recommending that he be returned to a regular classroom. His mother stated that he was easier to get along with and more cooperative at home.

His therapist stated that often they would spend the majority of the time in their sessions chatting, having an enjoyable, lighthearted conversation about life as a teenager in today's world. The therapist would, once in a while, slip in insights about how he was looking at his past, his parents or at his situation in school, sometimes almost as an "oh, by the way" side comment. Yet as he relaxed and enjoyed himself more, these insights got through his early warning defense system and started to hit home. Once they became his insights, he was on his way.

Because of the subject matter of therapy, people get asked personal questions about highly charged issues and are asked to explore their blind spots. We often challenge the basic beliefs of a lifetime. If we do not have the clients' trust and rapport, if we have our own agenda, if we are reactive or judgmental about their decisions, if we get impatient, we cannot help nearly as well. Our ability to be patient and responsive is tied to our ability to see when the client can't take any more—to be able to back off in order to reestablish a mutually respectful feeling. Some of the most successful sessions with clients have occurred when we are able to back off and see they have had enough, to recognize that they can't take in any more, to spend the remainder of a session talking about sports, or dance or music or whatever that clients' hobbies and interests are.

Breaking Down Health Realization for Clients

The therapists with whom we work say if they can go into a class or counseling session with their minds free of self-conscious thoughts, they can discern more clearly what to talk about, when to talk about it and how to best present these ideas to their clients. The principles underlying this approach are not complex and can be explained in a fairly short time. However, getting clients to grasp them in a way that they are able to apply them to their own lives is a different matter. The key to getting these ideas across in a meaningful way is to discern when clients are in the frame of mind to hear something different from their learned ways of looking at life, and what they are ready to hear.

The Nature of Empowering Relationships

The quality of the relationship between therapist and client is the catalyst to change. In large part, that quality is determined by the helper's ability to gracefully navigate his own moods, to disconnect his well-being from the situation at hand, to keep his sense of humor, and to stay humble.

All people lose their bearings from time to time, and therapists are no exception to this rule. The deeper our level of understanding, the faster we can regain our equilibrium and composure. Remember, we can still help others effectively even if we are in a bad mood if we are honest with ourselves and our clients about what is going on. Modeling this understanding doesn't mean that therapists are saints; it does mean that they give themselves the same honesty, respect, and compassion that they give to their clients.

Contaminants to Teaching

Earlier I talked about the importance of the therapists' ability to be compassionate and maintain their own well being. Many helpers lose their own good feelings when they commiserate in the name of caring. When we commiserate, we join our clients in looking to the past or to outside circumstances as the source of their problems and their well-being. Many therapists become tempted to commiserate in order to gain their clients' trust or friendship, to prove that they were listening or to show that they can identify with their clients' pain.

When therapists commiserate, unwittingly we are colluding with our clients' view of reality. We are subtly confirming that the best they can do is to try to cope in a hostile, untrustworthy world. We are unwittingly feeding the ego's need to prove itself by reinforcing their current strategies for dealing with life. Commiseration is tantamount to telling clients that they are indeed products of their past and their circumstances. In the name of helping we are still pointing outward, in the direction of their past or their situation as the source of their current woes. While this usually occurs in the guise of helping, it often becomes a barrier to change, particularly to empowerment as it exacerbates feelings of helplessness and hopelessness.

While commiseration should be avoided in the therapy process, compassion is essential to establish the trust and rapport that characterize a good environment for learning. When we are compassionate, we acknowledge that our clients are suffering without losing ourselves in their problems or their perspective. Genuine compassion allows us to care without losing respect for our clients' ability to help themselves.

Other states of mind that interfere with our ability to help include paternalistic or condescending attitudes. If we believe our clients should be doing better or that they are lazy or bad, a mutually respectful relationship—the foundation for success in therapy—is impossible to establish. Further, if we have limited expectations for what our clients will be able to achieve, their expectations for themselves will follow suit and they will feel less hopeful about the possibility for real change. On the other hand, when we hold people against the expectations of society, we are imposing pressure that they may not be able to endure, or ready to handle at the moment. In addition, we are less likely to notice small but meaningful changes in their feelings and behavior.

As long as a therapist can maintain genuine compassion they can help. As we learn to avoid the contaminants of talking down to clients or seeing them as their pathology, we can point them in the direction of psychological health. Clearly knowing that people carry their past via their habits of thought, we will not do any damage. While clients may be living in pain, it is pain they are usually adjusted to coping with, as part of their strategy for dealing with life. We can only make it worse by emphasizing or exaggerating it. We can facilitate making things better by pointing people toward something nicer.

Reducing Therapist Stress and Burnout

The burnout rate among clinical psychologists has been all too high over the last decade. It is attributable in part to the barriers mentioned above to the therapists well being and in part to lack of seeing permanent, positive change in their clients. In fact, we have had many professionals who had left the field of mental health for other careers tell us that it was just too hard, they never saw much hope for their clients. They said that they felt constantly burdened by their own doubts about their ability to help, as well as by the clients' chronic suffering.

This approach to therapy has the potential to reverse that trend. Therapists trained in this approach report that rather than fighting burnout, they look forward to going to work and seeing their clients each day. It is highly satisfying to help people move away from chronic negative patterns of thought, feelings and behaving to a more clear-eyed, positive outlook on life. Therapists enjoy the pleasant, respectful atmosphere of each counseling session and their clients' company. They are grateful that their clients catch on to what is being taught in ways that help them deal with stressful situations in positive ways. They trust that positive shifts in a clients outlook will lead to permanent changes in that clients' behavior.

More than anything else, therapists trained in this approach are grateful for the personal well-being that comes with a deeper understanding of this model's underlying principles—the same understanding that makes them so effective in their work. They can put their setbacks into perspective with the understanding that in the end, each of us can be responsible only for our own mental health. They can feel good at the end of every day, knowing that they gave their work their best shot; that they did their best to make a genuine difference in their clients' lives.

As therapists begin to live with a quieter mind themselves, they are able to see their work and their clients fresh every day as well. If they go home at the end of a day feeling frustrated about where a client seems stuck or confused, they are able to more easily relax and clear their heads in a way that leads to new insights about how to get through to that particular client. They are more likely to notice what their clients have already learned, notice subtle shifts in their clients thinking and know where to go next with each client.

With a quieter mind ourselves, we are continually having new insights about what we are teaching, about how to get it across effectively in a therapeutic modality, and about how to empower clients to better help themselves. All of these things tend to keep our work alive and engaging. People have remarked, after seminars that I or my colleagues do, that it is remarkable, and refreshing for them, to see professionals who have been in the field as long as we have appear as excited and enthusiastic about our work as we are.

It is exciting for us to know that this is the way our lives can be, and that these feelings and insights will continually deepen in ways that improve our abilities to help our clients. It is rewarding to see the health in our clients surface once we learn to get ourselves out of the way more and more. It is fascinating as we continually see finer distinctions between helping and controlling, being a teacher versus lecturing, between commiseration and compassion, between being seen as the expert and empowering clients to find their own wisdom. As we start to find nicer and nicer feelings and new levels of our own wisdom, from within ourselves, it becomes easier to point clients in the same direction in themselves. We recognize that we don't ever have to stop learning ourselves and becoming more effective in our work.

In the next chapter, I will be discussing the process of helping using this modality. From our experiences, there are discrete phases or logical steps that seemed to be consistent across therapists as they learned how to use this approach effectively. It is helpful for everyone of us to learn from these experiences. While these cannot be boiled down to, or used as set, cut and dried, techniques, they can act as guideposts and helpful clues as to how to keep ourselves on track. They help us know where we are and where we are going. However, we should never forget that the process always begins and ends with the health of the helper.

CHAPTER SIX

Rapport, Respect, and Insight: The Process of Therapy

In this chapter I will attempt to share what we have learned over the last fifteen years of studying this paradigm about how best to conduct therapy, or any helping relationship. In this model the bad news is that there is no set, predetermined method or structure for counseling. The good news is that, once we have applied these ideas to our own experience to understand how thought works everyday in our lives, we are better able to connect with the client's immediate experience. We can then relate to their subjective reality in a way that facilitates teaching the logic of this model and leads to positive change.

This chapter is intended to provide a broad brush overview of therapy. An entire text could easily be written covering the subtleties of each of the topics in this chapter, clarifying how we break these phases or steps down even more when training therapists and counsellors. This chapter is not meant to be exhaustive or to cover in an in-depth manner all the challenges and dynamics therapists run into in practice using this model. This chapter is merely intended to provide an overview of how the logic of the paradigm is generally applied to the therapy process.

P.O.M./Health Realization practitioners call on their personal understanding of the three basic elements of human functioning—mind, thought, and consciousness—and how these elements interact, to help clients. The goal of therapy, or any helping relationship, as I see it now, is to assist the person learn to recognize their innate mental health and how their thinking effects it. These insights or ideas always form the backdrop of Health Realization therapy yet they may or may not be discussed directly at any point in the therapy process. In essence every client contact is unique, both due to the unique needs and readiness of that client, and to what they have learned or realized already about thought and their mental health.

Teaching About Thought Versus Manipulating Thought

No-one can change or control the thoughts of another. We would never be presumptuous enough to attempt to change people's thinking. Rather we attempt to help clients regain power over their own thinking process. Our work is based on the premise that it is possible to give people a practical understanding of the role of thought. In Chapter One I stated that people who were exposed to pilot programs that illustrated how belief systems work benefited more than people in other forms of intervention methods. Yet at the time, our understanding of how people's thinking works to impact their day to day lives was extremely primitive.

Since those early days we have learned a great deal ourselves about how to teach people about the way that thought combines with our consciousness to create the appearance of reality. We attempt to teach people that the way things look to them is always a combination of the natural flow of their healthy thought process usually mixed with some form of conditioned thought. We have found that this kind of learning occurs faster the more we are able to make it relevant to their world, to their perceptions, to their immediate problems and concerns.

No P.O.M./Health Realization practitioner would claim that they are able to help everyone. There are always people who resist changing their outlook, or with whom these ideas do not connect. There are people who can't imagine having the wherewithal or the presence of mind to resolve their own problems. However, this understanding seems to take hold when it is presented in a way that enables clients to solve their problems and learn to feel better on their own. Teaching people about thought and their innate intelligence sparks insights that set the change process in motion. The therapist may talk about the healthy thought process in ways that they can then directly relate to client's experiences, to their ideas about mental health and what it takes to be that way. Hopefully, they can also discuss how conditioned thought works without getting the clients defensive or feeling wrong that they have been conditioned in certain ways.

Teaching Healthy Psychological Functioning

The best way we have found to introduce these ideas is a very impersonal approach that helps the client realize they are not at fault, but that these facts are true for everyone. The fact that people operate at times from nonfunctional, conditioned or insecure thinking is just the human condition. Thus Psychology of Mind or Health Realization practitioners may do more direct teaching than is done in many other forms of helping. But it still isn't teaching from a prescribed curriculum. It is a dynamic process of listening, targeting by honing in on the client's world view and then teaching how their experience of their lives is connected to the building blocks and the logic presented in the previous chapters.

Every therapist teaches this understanding in his or her own way. Nevertheless, it is possible to provide an overview of the general direction of treatment. We have also found that there are useful guidelines for proceeding through various phases of the psychotherapy process. What I mean here by phases is that there are things that once done, contribute to making the steps that may come after that easier to accomplish. Still, this is not a cookbook situation. Therapists still must use their wisdom and mental clarity in the moment to decide where to go next.

Prior to going into the different phases of the helping process, I want to cover a few things for the student that might hinder, or inadvertently create barriers to help in using this model. These are things that we have observed over the years that seem to be important in using this approach, and probably would be things to look out for when using any approach.

The Technique Trap

As the field of psychology has developed, various clinical techniques have emerged to address specific client diagnoses. Consequently, many therapists expect to start the counseling process by diagnosing the client's problem and applying the appropriate technique to solve that type of problem.

The use of this kind of methodology assumes that there are many different causes and avenues for relief of people's emotional problems. A Psychology of Mind therapist would try instead to understand how that person is misusing their thinking, and what they know or do not know about the thought process. They know that everyone's problems can manifest in myriad different ways, because people learn to think differently, from their unique combination of experiences. Yet they would work from the understanding that everyone is using the same common denominator, thought, to maintain their unique version of things.

In researching more and more the role of thought in life, we found all technique-based methodology to have a generic defect. The trouble with these approaches is that any technique, no matter how powerful, is only as good as the client thinks it is. If the role of thought, as a common denominator in the process of finding relief, doesn't become apparent, using any technique can point both the therapist and the client outside for solutions—away from the innate wisdom and capacity for understanding that provides the client with access to their own answers. The client usually is tempted instead to depend on a set of techniques. In this sense, any technique is one step removed from the person's inner wisdom. This is why we often notice that clients who have used similar techniques, whether in therapy or in self help groups, often develop somewhat of a habitual dependence on that group of techniques.

If therapists aren't looking at thought as the common denominator producing any behavior, it is tempting to turn to an external technique to help their clients. When those techniques don't work, frustrated therapists may compound the problem by confronting their clients or making them feel guilty. For example in the past, when we did seminars for couples or offered programs on stress, we often did exercises using techniques for certain therapeutic purposes. We noticed however that each participant drew different conclusions or interpreted the point of the exercise differently. Instead of linking that back to thought, we forced our explanation of the benefits of each technique. This kind of manipulation met with resistance from some. From those who complied with our ideas and felt the technique had helped them, the technique tended to become a therapeutic ritual. As such it worked to different degrees as a crutch or support for feeling better when that person sought relief.

Over time, we found that none of our techniques were as powerful or as flexible and accurate as the therapist's personal insights. Therapists would have insights at every moment in therapy, or in teaching. These insights involved grasping what the client is thinking and how their thinking is effecting their state of mind. Therefore, every therapy session or class naturally follows a different path as the therapist learns to trust her own wisdom to reveal what to teach in the moment. The therapist is also responsible for noticing any insecure thoughts or negative feelings—her own or the client's—that could interfere with her ability to see what to teach or her client's ability to hear it.

Why Exploring Dysfunction Doesn't Help

Historically, therapists have felt that helping people work through negative feelings was a prerequisite to creating positive change. From experience with previous approaches to therapy, my colleagues and I knew that encouraging people to revisit their past traumas made their insecurity rise. When we encouraged clients to act out their negative feelings, they felt worse as they took on these feelings. When we treated people as one and the same with their problems, their problems tended to "lock in" and become more real. When we delved into their problems when they were feeling insecure, they became more anxious and disturbed.

As our research continued, we saw that people were helped much more by learning about their intrinsic health than by exploring the details of their dysfunction. People were helped more when they learn to relate to the experience of their healthy states of mind rather than to their diagnoses. They felt relieved and helped more by learning that they could put their past behind them rather than reentering a horrible experience. And we found that a supportive, relaxed, and respectful atmosphere helps clients to recognize that their emotional disturbances are states of mind produced by insecure habits of thinking, rather than by fixed personality traits.

In this paradigm, insecure thoughts and whatever feelings they generate are what stand in the way of mental health. Our continuing observations have shown us that people almost automatically move into healthier states of mind whenever they feel relaxed and don't feel judged, guilty, or upset—as they might be if they were reliving the worst moments of their lives. At first it was difficult for us to understand how this worked. We had been trained to take negative feelings and perceptions more seriously. We had learned that positive feelings were suspect as "flights into health" or avoidance of the real problem. Our own biases obscured the logic of noticing that people were automatically more rational, more responsive and wiser when they were relaxed and had nothing on their minds.

Clarifying the Nature of Mental Health

We have found that the single most helpful thing we as therapists can teach our clients is that they always have direct access to a healthier state of mind. Even if they experience just a fleeting glimpse of this state—a single moment of ease and noncontingent self-assurance—they begin to see that genuinely living in health is possible. This is particularly the case if they recognize that they didn't first have to change anything, do anything, or relive their past to engage that state of mind. It is like realizing that you can change the gears of your car, from drive to neutral or vice versa without first having to go through reverse.

As my colleagues and I began to train other therapists, we found that the first thing we had to do—and sometimes the most difficult—was teaching them to look for the health in their clients. Seeing health enabled therapists to see their clients as students rather than as "patients" and to reframe their jobs as teachers. Therapists learned their job was not to help people process the past, but to teach them about their innate capacity for health, insight, and happiness. They also learned to explain how accessing a healthier perspective helped them put the past in perspective and leave it behind. Clients would survey their past from a clearer, wiser and more impersonal vantage point that allowed them to move beyond its effects.

Rather than address our clients' behavior directly, we learned to show them how their behavior was linked to their thinking. Rather than help them express their negative feelings, we helped them explore how negative feelings and thoughts are connected to moods. We taught that moods can fluctuate from moment to moment without any apparent reason—and how important is it to notice these changes. We asked clients to describe the feelings they have when they are relaxed and are not thinking about anything in particular. We attempted to clarify the difference between common sense or insight and conditioned thought. As we found ways to more clearly describe these relationships, we saw more immediate and sustained results.

Establishing the Therapeutic Relationship

My clinic once had a client who was a nurse at a local hospital. She called one day about a patient who had become her friend during the year he had been coming in with back problems. He was an older man with no family in the area and had been laid off from his job as a mid-level engineer in a company that was down-sizing due to lost contracts. His first job interview was discouraging. He was told the company preferred to hire people right out of college. He started to assume that no company would want him at his age and salary expectations.

The man applied for unemployment. Due to a paperwork mix-up, he didn't receive his first check and was getting down to his last few dollars. One day he called his only friend, the nurse, to tell her he was going to drink a pitcher of beer and then walk in front of a truck. She couldn't convince him to come into the hospital to talk to a social worker. She called us in a panic to ask for help.

She said her friend was extremely depressed and seemed serious about his intention to commit suicide. She told us where we could find him. When our counsellor arrived at the bar, he was already inebriated and hostile. He stated that he didn't want anyone to try to talk him out of what he intended to do.

Asking if he could join him, the counsellor sat down and began talking about how he had been in the Navy, too. They sat and shared war stories and ended up having a few laughs about the crazy things that happen in the military. After about a half hour, the counsellor could tell that the man was in a better mood and that they had established rapport. He had connected with his world in a way that made sense to him and he saw the counselor as a comrade rather than as a threat.

Now, he was in a position to help this person see that things weren't really as bad as they seemed to him at that moment. He had moved into a state of mind where he could consider other options and see them as reasonable. After they talked for quite some time and he gained a little more perspective on his situation, one of our staff accompanied him to the VA hospital to have the social worker straighten out his benefit problem. Today, the man is reemployed and content, and all of us are grateful for the rapport we were able to establish on the blackest day of his life.

Establishing genuine rapport with the client is the essential first step of any therapy. The type of rapport that is important in this model is the kind that enables us to see our clients as equals and appreciate their capacity for insights and change. It enables our clients to trust us, to know that we will be in their corner no matter what, that we won't let their problems or behavior throw us off. It is essentially an esteeming and empowering kind of rapport. Establishing this climate in the therapist-client relationship does not foster dependence or resistance. It does not foster pain or discomfort, but rather self assurance and hope. It is uplifting rather than humiliating.

It is our own sense of well-being, rather than anything we say or teach, that enables therapists to engage clients in a relaxed, comfortable way. Our ability to help clients feel at ease with us helps raise their mood to the level where they can listen. The relief and gratitude that accompany even a momentary rise of mood grease the wheels for further positive change.

Establishing rapport with clients doesn't hinge on how much we like them. It doesn't depend on what we think about their current behavior. Our job as therapists is to see beyond our clients' personality and behavior to the core of health that lies within, to see past their conditioned beliefs to their essential innocence. The therapy process cannot be as effective without the lubricant of rapport, so it's important for therapists to take as much time as is necessary to establish a safe, friendly feeling with clients. In the process, you are modeling a way to see things with less urgency. Don't be afraid to share stories about your own ups and downs to help your clients see that people are all the same in terms of how we work psychologically. You want them to realize that you work the way they do, and that your understanding of accessing health can help them as well. Of course, with some clients it is easier to establish rapport than with others. Some may come in mistrustful of authority figures, some will be hostile and embarrassed. Others may feel at first that you are not taking their problems seriously enough. These are all preconceptions to look for and worked through as part of building rapport.

What follows are some other practical guidelines for enhancing the effectiveness of the therapy process. Although this may sound like beating a dead horse, I want to state again that these guidelines are not techniques. They are not meant to be memorized and done in any rigidly structured "rote" way. They are observations concerning what we have learned in clinical trails and other helping situations in terms of the flow and phases of an effective helping process.

Maintaining the Tone; Establish a Light-hearted Atmosphere

Before you take on your clients' problems, it helps greatly to first establish a light-hearted tone of hopefulness and reassurance. Be patient and relaxed. You are attempting to model the ability to step back and reflect from a wiser perspective, to help them understand the situation without getting caught up in their habitual emotional reactions. Kid around with them, ask them about hobbies, share stories, chat, and engage them as friends.

If they feel secure and respected as your equal, they will hang in there. Establishing this kind of therapeutic climate also helps clients suspect that things may not be as bad as they look to them at the moment.

It is important to be able to do this without being flippant or disrespectful. If you have compassion and are sensitive to the fact that people are suffering, the client won't think you are taking their problems lightly. At the same time, you can provide a feeling that things aren't as bad as they look at the moment.

Check the Tone—And Your Intent—Regularly

Can you distinguish if you are genuinely in a state of service? Check for any contaminated feelings—i.e., do you feel a need to impress your clients? Are you seeing your clients as peers in terms of their capacity for insight and health? Are you demonstrating that they don't have to do anything or prove anything to earn your respect? Once is not enough; to ensure that you maintain the rapport you have established, revisit these questions throughout the therapy process.

Listening For Understanding

Once you and your client have established a feeling of rapport and ease in the therapeutic relationship, the next important piece is listening. Our job here is not to elicit the details of our clients' problems. Rather, we should be listening for the client's most basic underlying assumptions about life, because these beliefs are precisely what stand in the way of mental health—and they are so ingrained and feel so real that they are part of the client's unconscious. Even if the client is not aware of their most deeply ingrained beliefs, it helps the therapist greatly to recognize these assumptions for what they are. They can then see where to start to help that person move out of this framework of beliefs.

Always remember that thought and consciousness work together to create the appearance of reality. The picture we see of our lives is like a completed jigsaw puzzle. All our thinking fits together to make up a picture of life that appears real to us. We normally do not see its pieces as being made up of thought. You are looking for a way to illustrate pieces that the client can more readily recognize as beliefs, as a way of pointing them toward an even deeper understanding of how the entire puzzle is created. At some point you also may want to help them identify the core beliefs, the most basic assumptions that hold the entire puzzle together.

Listening and the Subconscious

Different theories in psychology have different definitions of the subconscious, including what it is and what it does. Many theorists feel that there are actual entities, archetypes or common themes in our subconscious. I would respond that there are only more thoughts, thoughts that are out of our awareness, thoughts that we think are reality, not thoughts. If we imagine the subconscious as anything within our mind that we have potential access to, but have not yet realized, there would then be two parts of the subconscious. The first is those beliefs that are so ingrained from our earliest experiences that they are not seen as beliefs, but just the way things are in life. The second aspect of the subconscious is something really beautiful, it is that person's innate intelligence, their wisdom, their ability to deeply enjoy their life and handle things in a mature, responsible way, relying on that inner core of health. A therapists job is to assist the person release both their conscious and their unconscious hold on their belief system and tap into the mother lode of their innate wisdom that is the deepest part of the subconscious, yet is directly accessible for use in daily life.

Listening for understanding lets us know how best to help our clients, as it triggers our natural insights. Our ability to listen to our clients with understanding rather than from preconceptions or judgments also shows them how we would like them to listen to us. Listening for understanding—on either side—cannot occur if we are labeling and categorizing our clients according to a conceptual framework of our own devising. Any preconceptions will get in the way. Thinking that we know where someone is coming from before we really do know can also get in the way.

When we listen to our clients, it is with the understanding that they are doing their best to cope given how life looks to them right now. Their strategies for coping seem important as the best they can do, when life looks the way it does most of the time. These coping styles have also become attached to their self concept and ideas about self worth. When we can maintain our own well-being and see their innocence and effort, the insecure feelings which block insights begin to abate so that they can listen with less resistance and realize their ability to live beyond their learned beliefs.

As we discussed in Chapter Three, most people develop a personality and coping style that is firmly based on their ingrained beliefs about what they need to do to survive. These strategies—which often include defensiveness, toughness, and anger—are only necessary within the framework of their own belief system. So, in a sense, coping strategies serve as an alternative to mental health.

Ultimately, our job as therapists is to plumb beneath the personality to the place where innate wisdom and unconditional self-esteem reside in their subconscious—and to teach clients to access this precious resource on their own. It is exciting to show people how to move beyond coping to take advantage of their deepest, wisest feelings—and to enjoy more compassion, love, and contentment in their lives. Even if our clients reach only the tip of the iceberg of these kinds of feelings, the quality of their life will improve. We can then point them in the direction of having even more beneficial insights. All of this starts with listening.

Respectful Inquiry

Respectful inquiry is a preferable mode of listening, whether you are a counselor, a boss or a friend. Rather than judging or analyzing someone else's world from our biases, we want to become fascinated with how things look to them. We should be curious and intrigued by how they put things together. Ask questions because you want to know more about your clients and their views of the world. Ask because you are genuinely interested, not because you want to judge or change them. If you are not respectful and interested now, they will not give you full answers. Nor will they be able to hear your insights or ideas without feeling wrong or resistant.

Listening to Understand Their Beliefs

Attempt to hear past their "surface" ideas about their problems. You want to keep listening and asking until you hit the rock bottom of their logic—to the point where if they began to question some of those fundamental notions about life, the host of ideas built on those beliefs would disappear spontaneously. Both the therapist and client will usually know when this occurs, as they will see how everything else that is going on with that client can be tied back into those basic beliefs.

It is essential, of course, that we understand those beliefs accurately. If we did not listen well enough, we can easily assign another cause to the way our clients behave by extrapolating from our experience with other people. In fact, one of the biggest barriers to deep listening is our own experience and training. We may feel that we already know what a client's problem is before we hear it. To accomplish the level of listening that is necessary here, we need to be comfortable in a state of not knowing so that we can open our ears and our hearts to what we are hearing.

When we truly listen, clients are more likely to feel understood and appreciated, making it safer for them to listen to whatever we feel moved to teach. If we have really listened, teaching can appear as easy as falling off a log. A good analogy is a great athlete who makes his sport look simple, although we know it isn't. That athlete has practiced the basics so much that they are second nature. Practicing the art of listening makes knowing what to teach almost like second nature. It begins to be more obvious, and clients may be surprised at how quickly the therapist hones in on their reality. Again, we need to keep monitoring the level of rapport we have established. If it slips, anything we have to say will fall on deaf ears.

Teaching in Real Time

Teaching health realization in real time means being able to assess where the client is, in her thinking, at any moment. In a relaxed state of mind, once we have really listened deeply to our clients, the therapist then knows where to begin teaching. They will have an insight about what will hit that client as being either true or useful about the logic behind the principles they are teaching. A recognition of how their thoughts can work either for or against them is, for most clients, ninety percent of the battle. The healthy thought process then takes over and does the rest in a very ordinary but effective way. Our insights about how to connect these principles to their world trigger their insights about how to improve their lives, and master their own psychological functioning.

When we are teaching in real time, we wait until we have an insight about what to teach, trusting that our innate intelligence will deliver it if we quiet our minds to receive it. Appropriate examples, stories, and analogies simply float into our heads when we are teaching in real time. This does not mean that at times our insights still won't be appreciated by clients. We may have to come at it from several different angles to make the logic relevant and compelling to the client. However, the process is one of having it be more and more apparent that we are gently unearthing the client's key blind spots while finding ways to help them relate to their healthy thinking process.

Teaching in real time means sharing insights you are having at the moment that will help your clients take the next step to improve their lives. Teaching in real time means helping people see both the possibility and the value of changing their outlook now.

Teaching in Their World

It is important for your clients to know that the principles of psychological functioning you are teaching apply equally to all human beings—rich and poor, black and white, young and old. Every one of us has insecure beliefs acquired in childhood. Likewise, lack of understanding—and fluctuating levels of understanding from moment to moment—are part of the human condition. Everyone develops coping mechanisms to compensate for their perceived deficiencies or life's tribulations. We all have many years invested in these coping styles, whether they work or not. And everyone views the way they cope as the right way—until they learn about the source of a healthier and more secure reality. It is important for your clients to be able to connect with the rest of humanity in this way.

At the same time, it is important for you to connect with people in their own context. The goal of teaching is to link clients' views of life to the principles of Psychology of Mind in a way that makes sense to them. This means we must have a good feel for our clients' "reality." Do not try to convince, cajole, or pressure people into accepting anything you are saying. If what you say rings true within their frame of reference, they will buy it. Also, you should be careful not to judge when you describe the logical consequences of your clients' negative actions. You are attempting to show them the consequences of their choices, not blame them for something they've already done.

Teach the Power of Hope

People cannot change until they glimpse that change is possible, so engendering a feeling of hope is among the therapist's most important assignments. We do this by empathizing and by looking for innate health and strength instead of pathology and problems. As Psychology of Mind therapists, we are always teaching people how thought works with consciousness, and how to reconnect with their innate capacity for health. There is no guesswork involved in the direction of what we are teaching. But each therapist tailors delivery of these facts to touch each client in the context of his core beliefs. We want to illustrate that their beliefs may not hold as much importance as they feel they do, while we also point toward and demonstrate access to a better, more productive and secure vantage point.

We once had a chronically depressed patient who said she had glimmers of hope from time to time, but would then lapse back into her habitual hopelessness. As we listened to her, we saw that one good entry point for teaching would be to talk about what moods do to our thinking. We could then show her what to do about her thinking when she was feeling depressed. Rather than taking it so seriously, she could ignore it, think about other things, and wait for her mood level to change. This approach was just the opposite of what she had been doing, which was to use her low-mood thinking to find more reasons why she should be depressed, writing off her hopeful moments as aberrant flukes.

The therapist's state of mind is what determines how quickly and accurately you know what to teach. If you start feeling insecure about needing to be the expert or pressured to come up with something brilliant, these thoughts are mental static that effects your ability to listen. Listening works best when we have no interest in knowing what we will teach until it becomes obvious in the form of an insight.

Teaching in real time also involves asking questions in a way that allows people to come up with their own answers. The ability to think up these kinds of questions comes as a natural flow of ideas when we are teaching in real time. For example, we may want to ask a parent how she could have handled being upset at her child in some way other than hitting the child. We may want to ask a depressed person to consider ways that they can keep from dwelling on thoughts that are keeping them depressed. We may want to ask an addicted client what options are occurring to them now other than taking a drink when they notice that compulsive urge.

When we teach, we talk less about how we can help clients solve their specific problems and more about how they can find or regain their ability to solve their own problems. This can be tricky, because clients often think they want more concrete help. They want to know what steps to take to change their behavior or feel better. Learning to notice the quality of their thinking and monitoring the level of their moods may feel passive at first, but it is the key to taking control of their own thinking—and their own mental health.

Assessing Progress and Making Adjustments

Noticing Small Changes

We can assess our clients' progress by noticing how they are feeling, looking, and carrying themselves. Initially, we should notice that they seem more relaxed with themselves and others. They can exchange ideas and stories with less fear or defensiveness. They behave with more confidence and assertion. Even tiny changes in mood, appearance and rational thinking states are significant indicators of progress. Notice them—then appreciate and enjoy them with your clients.

Keeping the Good Feeling in Place

When we are teaching, we can assess how well we are doing by the feeling in the air. If our interaction is successful, the feeling should be hopeful and enthusiastic. If we are off-track—if the person isn't grasping what we're teaching or is not having positive insights, we need to stop and rebuild rapport, listen more deeply, or revisit how we've been teaching to see if there are better ways to connect.

In this chapter I touched on the key elements of how therapy is done using this model. As I mentioned at the beginning of this chapter, these qualities of the helping process apply in any relationship. The process of building rapport, of listening deeply to someone else's world, of assisting them learn how to use their own common sense and tap into their innate well being, are all part of any empowering relationship. As a therapist, we usually have more permission to be a teacher, but it helps to remember always that what we really are is a facilitator. We are facilitating the other person realizing the resources they already have in them for health, insight and wisdom.

Hopefully, I have been able to describe the focus and direction of therapy in ways that clarify the logic of this approach. An entire textbook could be written about the therapy that has emerged from this model. This chapter was intended merely to touch on key elements and how the logic of the principles underlying this approach dictate the direction and process of treatment.

More than anything, we want our clients to learn that they already have mental health, that it is their birthright. We want them to learn that the state of health can be submerged by beliefs, but that it bobs to the surface automatically when we loosen our grip on our judgments and preconceptions. And we want them to know that in a state of health, our wisdom provides the insights, motivation, and self-esteem we need to bring our own problems to successful conclusions.

The process described in this chapter is, for the therapist, the ideal way therapy would work. It insures that clients do not become chronically dependent on us. It also shows clients the power of the human spirit, and the inner resources they can bring to bear on solving their own problems. Many people have asked us whether such a model of helping can generalize to people who are normally outside of the kinds of clients who would go into a clinic or practice for therapy. In fact some the most positive, impressive outcomes to date have come from applying this health realization model in severely disadvantaged, underserved communities. In these settings it has been presented as an approach to prevention, early intervention and community empowerment. The next chapter will present these applications.

CHAPTER SEVEN

Education, Prevention, and Early Intervention

Psychology of Mind approach has proven highly effective in the areas of prevention and early intervention. It is in this area that there has been the most widespread applications of this approach. It is in this area that there has been the most data collected in the course of pilot programs in a wide variety of settings and cultures. This approach has shown highly promising results in extremely hard core settings where other approaches have failed to make a significant dent in serious problems of drugs, crime, school failure and alienation.

Since 1987, my colleagues and I have conducted demonstration programs across a wide variety of ethnic groups, schools, and inner city neighborhoods, as well as in middle class and other communities in Miami, Tampa, and Bradenton, Florida, New York, Denver, Honolulu, and Vallejo, Stockton, and Oakland, California. The inspiring results we have seen with high-risk, inner-city young people and their families have been the focus of special NBC and PBS programs and have attracted the attention of foundations and research institutes nationwide.

As you know, our approach focuses on helping people gain access to their innate mental health rather than attacking or shoring up their weaknesses. Indeed, the focus on strength is not exclusive to Psychology of Mind; throughout the practice of psychology, researchers are becoming more excited about the idea of building on people's capacity for health. In the area of prevention, this new focus has been described as a paradigm shift from looking at problems to looking at positive health in a way that has produced competancy models in psychology and psychiatry.

This shift of focus has come about, in part, because a growing body of research reveals that a surprising percentage of young people raised in dysfunctional families and disadvantaged neighborhoods manage to bounce back from trauma to become mature, responsible adults. In these longitudinal studies there were no outside interventions. These youth had to rely on their own inner resources. The researchers in these studies wondered how this was possible, and settled on a new something they called "resiliency" as the answer.

From study to study, resilient people tend to exhibit: 1) a positive outlook, 2) self-esteem and a feeling of being in control of their lives, 3) the ability to defer gratification to achieve long-term goals, 4) the ability to use critical thinking and planning skills, and 5) a sense of humor and good social skills. Many intervention programs develop curricula for teaching each of these basic characteristics. Most of these intervention programs assume that these attributes must be instilled or taught, or somehow put into at-risk youth from outside.

The notion that mental health, including resiliency, is our most natural state of mind is generally not taken into account. Researchers grounded in traditional psychological theories tend to attribute resiliency to the same variables that "cause" dysfunction, genetic, early childhood, and environmental influences. They make the assumption that positive habits need to be learned or programmed into children in the same way that negative habits or an alienated outlook has been conditioned.

Psychology of Mind practitioners and programs, on the other hand, rely on the concept that mental health is the birthright of every human being, and that the helper's job is to help people reconnect with this precious innate resource. We posit that learning to think from an insecure frame of reference creates an overlay of alienated attitudes and behavior. The basic assumption behind our intervention programs is that once this overlay is removed, the strength of the human spirit will help a person put things back on track by providing self righting mechanisms and a more solid immunity to serious psychological problems.

We are in no way denying that growing up under adverse circumstances makes it harder for people to keep their heads above water. We are not advocating that any society should allow these conditions to persist. What we are learning is that no one's inner strengths, their spirit or true nature as a worthwhile human being, can be totally crushed. These attributes always have the potential for being stronger than the scars wrought from a person's upbringing and their past.

As one author put it after he had reviewed a national study of youth who had survived extremely dysfunctional childhood environments: "The challenge is not to keep trying to repair what was damaged, but instead to reawaken what is already within, to cultivate those qualities of heart and spirit that are available in this very moment" (Mueller, Legacy of the Heart, 1992).

The Challenge

Before we launched our first intervention programs, in two Miami public housing projects, we surveyed the middle-school students there to determine their attitudes toward school and family and their expectations for the future. Most of the students we tested thought they would never finish school and would end up on the streets. Psychologically, most had already dropped out: 64% were failing and the truancy rate approached 80%. The students who were still in school caused frequent problems and had an extremely high incidence of discipline referrals.

These young people told us they did not like their teachers. They attributed negative motives to most adults. They scored low on the self-esteem scales and high on scales measuring hostility, depression, and anxiety. We found it difficult to engage them because many put up a tough, cynical front.

For many students from these projects, by the end of first grade, they already felt they couldn't learn, that teachers were against them, that other students would not accept them, and so on. These expectations led to self-defeating behaviors, which in turn led to disciplinary measures that only exacerbated their low expectations and negative behavior. For instance, let's say a second-grader talks back to a teacher. He's sent to the principal's office and given detention. Understandably upset, he picks a fight on the school bus and is suspended, which only reinforces his perception that school is not for him. By the time this boy enters middle school his negative beliefs run deep.

Laying The Foundation

We are not denying that these youth lived amid horrible circumstances. The more our society can do to eliminate poverty and racism, the less stress there will be, leaving more room for feelings that promote resiliency and less for feelings that create anxiety or alienation. If people grow up with less prejudice and fewer societal barriers to success, it makes sense that they will be less likely to take on alienated or insecure patterns of thinking. However negative a person's past has been, we felt that we were learning something that could help, something practical about how they carried that past through time as an alienated pattern of thought.

We did everything we could to reduce sources of stress when we began our public housing programs in 1987. We helped our clients with emergency rental needs, paid utility bills, and provided supplementary food, clothing, and physical security. We offered job training and day care assistance. We worked hard to make circumstances easier for our clients. We wanted there to be as few barriers as we could singlehandedly influence to people being able to make improvements in their lives.

At the same time, we never lost sight of the bottom line which was the basis of our grant applications and overall intervention strategy. We wanted to see what could happen when people learned some practical ideas about how to take charge of their own thinking. We hypothesized that they would begin to handle adversity with more hope and self-respect and find ways to improve their circumstances both as a community and on their own. We trusted that our clients' innate intelligence would surface as soon as they could drop their attachment to alienated or insecure patterns of thinking. We suspected and hoped that the buoyancy of the human spirit would deliver the resiliency they needed to frame their prospects and capabilities in a more hopeful light.

Levels of Intervention

In my graduate school days, researchers in the prevention field differentiated among intervention levels as follows: Primary prevention strategies provided immunity before any pathology emerged. Secondary interventions were deployed at the first sign of a problem. And tertiary, or remedial, interventions were used to address serious problems. Our pilot programs redefined and addressed all three levels of need. What has come to be known as the Health Realization/Community Empowerment model works with the same independent variable, the person's understanding of their own thinking, at each level of prevention.

The logic of Psychology of Mind has it that the strength of a deviant outlook hinges on the level of insecurity ingrained in one's thinking. Because insecure thinking feeds on itself, the sooner we could reverse the downward spiral of self-defeating thinking and behaving, the better. We also wanted the public agencies and private organizations, the culture and society around these high risk populations, to better appreciate their capacity for healthy, productive functioning. We wanted these groups to understand how they could engage and build on that capacity.

If our charge was to strengthen the core of mental health that combats insecurity, we reasoned that primary prevention efforts should teach parents to bring out the best in their children by engaging their natural self-esteem and creating secure, nurturing environments. Secondary interventions should also alleviate sources of insecurity in the environment and teach children to recognize the strength of their innate intelligence and self-esteem.

Tertiary prevention would involve one-on-one counseling to help alienated individuals regain a broader perspective. In our third-level programs, interventions include intensive family counseling, referral to detoxification programs as needed, and follow-up support groups. We always try to see as many family members as possible at this stage, as well as bringing in other agencies, school administrators, teachers, and counselors.

Primary Prevention

If the adults around a child function in a healthier way, the buoyant nature of a child's mental health would argue that the child would probably respond in kind. This was the thinking behind our primary prevention programs. We assumed that enhancing the understanding, feelings, and interactions between young people and their parents and teachers would create home and school climates where security and self-esteem could flower. Specific programs at this level included resident leadership training, parent/administrator collaborations to improve school climate, resident-driven community development programs, and teacher training.

One of the first objectives was to identify potential community leaders. Offering a leadership training course at the local community college, we taught basic Health Realization principles, tying them to leadership styles that engender hope and cooperation. We found relevant ways to include ideas about our thinking habits, about separate realities and how people learn to interpret things. We talked about the difference between secure and insecure states of mind, and where people learn to think about themselves in self limiting ways. We presented our ideas about everyone's innate potential for a healthy, motivated outlook, and how that outlook surfaced in people.

Very early on, we observed that participants already were feeling better about themselves and getting along better with their neighbors. They let go of much of their frustration and hopelessness about their situation and grew confident that they could unite to change things for the better. Residents began to have ideas for issues to address and became interested in what resources they could tap into to address their problems.

As a result of the leadership classes, plus parenting classes and self-esteem support groups, one resident said: "Before, I would not help anyone out, but only participate in the gossip and finger-pointing. People have really changed, and now they will go out of their way to help and support each other."

As people began to apply the principles they learned in class, they established and strengthened relationships at home, work, and school. They saw ways to reduce stress in their lives. And they saw opportunities to help their children change their negative attitudes and problem behavior.

Prevention And Parenting

Long-term studies by independent researchers show that young people who are most at risk come from families where there is chronic conflict. In these studies, parents were in persistently low moods and allowed their moods to control their interactions with their children to create a pattern of habitual negative interactions and strained, mistrustful relationships.

These parents were critical and demeaning to their children. They weren't rational and consistent with discipline, nor did they display much affection. Their insecurity was such that they had trouble managing the stress in their lives and rarely made it through the day without a major upset. They took out their frustration on their children, whom they saw as an overwhelming burden. The climate that resulted was a breeding ground for insecurity, instability, hostility, and confusion.

We couldn't blame the parents for the harm they inflicted; the way they treated their children was consistent with how they were raised and with the way they saw their own lives. Parents, as well as their children had to put up with horrific circumstances. In our pretests the parents also scored higher on the hostility and depression scales, and low on the self esteem scales. They complained that their children did not mind them and that they had to go "upside the head" to control their kids.

We knew that creating healthier home environments had to be an urgent goal of our work in high risk neighborhoods. In our parent groups and classes we tried to connect the parent's self esteem and their habits of thinking about their lives with how they saw and responded to their children.

As we helped parents find more contentment for themselves, we saw them begin to use common sense with their children. As they became more self-assured, loving, and consistent, they learned not to take their moods out on their children. They listened better, were more interested and respectful. They became firm yet caring, guiding their children to make better decisions.

One of our clients had lived in public housing for more than 17 years. She was extremely depressed and had attempted suicide as a teenager after getting pregnant and dropping out of school in the ninth grade. She now had three children and had almost given them up several times. Her parents had convinced her that she was stupid and ugly and good for nothing. And she believed that she was a terrible mother.

After attending the leadership and parenting classes, she began to see how her insecure self-concept had mired her in depression and negative thinking about herself and her children. She found herself enjoying her children a little more and hitting them a little less. She started to take care of herself physically, to wear make-up and fix her hair. She joined the PTA at her children's school and became an officer.

Within a few months, this woman was attending a job training program. Always terrified of math, she learned to do division in a single day, observing that it was "a lot easier and more interesting than I thought it would be." After completing her G.E.D., she got a job in a convenience store and entered a nursing assistant training program. Today, she has moved her family out of public housing, is living with the father of her children, and holds a good full-time job. She found that her new, and solid feelings of self worth provided a powerful tool for change.

Teacher Training

Just as the health of parents was paramount in our parenting programs, the health of the teachers was the goal of our teacher training program. This training focused on the way moods and thinking influenced teachers perceptions of students, and vice versa. We helped teachers see how their moods shaped their ability to nurture healthy thinking in their students. We discussed how they viewed students from public housing and how that ingrained perception affected interactions with these students.

As a result of the training, teachers began to respond with more patience and understanding. They stopped taking the students' behavior as a personal affront. They recognized more often that these young people were doing their best given their learned expectations.

The teachers began to understand that alienation and problem behavior are products of insecurity. Consequently, when students caused problems, the teachers learned to see them as insecure rather than incorrigible, which brought the balm of compassion to the situation.

In their evaluations of the training, teachers reported that they were better able to manage classroom behavior and to engage students interest in the subject at hand. Teachers made such comments as: "First and foremost, I learned a lot about myself. I learned to think about the situation before reacting." "I learned to recognize bad moods as simply thoughts originating from me [which] can be controlled by me." "It has helped to put my mind at ease and raise my thought patterns to a saner level." "It has made me look into myself and how I look at others."

Teachers also reported that: "I never realized how my moods influence my class ... sometimes they seem to be in a good humor and ready to learn; at other times they seem ready to jump down my and each other's throats. Now, when my class seems edgy and up-tight, I step back and examine my moods and the signals I am putting out." "My compassion for students and parents has grown because of my awareness that you cannot always change another person, but you may be able to guide and assist." "I've become more aware of the source of low self-esteem in many of my students." "I have seen many errors in my handling of several situations that I hope to be able to remedy as they arise in the future."

Even in junior high, where problem behavior tends to accelerate, many young people improved dramatically, without individual counseling, when teachers and parents became more caring and respectful. Before long, the teachers found that themselves working with motivated students who wanted to learn. Rather than attempting to control or work hard to manage the students' behavior, the teachers found themselves struggling to stay ahead of their students' accelerated learning curves. They reported that the students were more cooperative and reliable in terms of doing assignments, asking for help, and completing work.

Documenting the Buoyancy of Health

Testing before and after our pilot programs showed that most of the young people we worked with had changed their outlook, expectations, and behavior significantly. Levels of conflict dropped dramatically in 87% of the families tested. Parents said their children were more cooperative and they could discuss things "in a more helpful and supportive manner."

Although our pilot programs were aimed at alienated youth, a happy side effect was that most of their parents either got jobs, enrolled in job training programs, or returned to school. When these adults regained their feelings of self-worth, they took it upon themselves, individually and as a group, to seek new resources and opportunities for employment, education, and community development.

As the neighborhood leaders and parents glimpsed the value of collective community action, they organized their own PTA groups and reorganized their resident council. The PTA met with the school principals and requested that teachers be trained to work more effectively with their children. They suggested changes in school discipline policies that would help keep their kids in school and requested remedial and after-school programs to help their children catch up. In return, they promised that their children would attend school. Overall, the first year of our program saw a 500% increase in parental involvement at school.

At the same time, the neighborhood leaders and parents started to work with the sheriff's department to organize a team police program. They worked with the housing authority and the state attorney's office to eliminate drug trafficking and diminish crime rates. They met with HUD officials to obtain funding to build a new community center to house a day-care program and after-school programs. They met with city authorities to get the park next door donated to the housing project, then installed athletic fields, started a basketball league, and wrote grants to buy playground equipment and subsidize after-school activities, field trips, and educational materials. They requested and enrolled in job training and employment programs delivered on site.

The resident council at one of the housing projects sponsored a fund raiser to benefit migrant families who had suffered severe economic consequences from a freeze that winter. By 1990 this project boasted one of the highest employment rates of any public housing project in that county and was the seat of leadership for the local African-American community.

By the end of the first year of the program, these neighborhoods had already undergone a significant change. People felt better about themselves and each other. They were beginning to see the light at the end of the tunnel in terms of improved prospects and were warmed by the spark of hope.

As the teenagers in these projects saw the culture of the community change and watched their parents take charge of their own lives, many came around on their own. Truants who dealt drugs came to our staff and asked for help in getting back in school. The students organized a student tenant council to learn about their self-esteem and their capacity to improve their lives. Truancy, delinquency, and problem behavior dropped, and many students who had been gang members or drug dealers began working with the police to form a youth crime watch, start a police athletic league, and organize an after-school tutoring program so they could catch up in school.

When we interviewed the students, many said they noticed changes in their outlook or their feelings about themselves only after the fact. They couldn't explain exactly when or how they had gained a different perspective on school, gangs, and motivation, which reinforced our findings that the innate capacity for health returns automatically when people are less self-conscious, or are taking an alienated frame of reference less seriously.

Secondary and Tertiary Interventions

Although changing the adults around them helped many young people, it didn't reach all of them. Some had developed habits of insecure thinking to the extent that they couldn't entertain any other frame of reference. And within an insecure reference frame, even positive change is threatening. If, for example, an at-risk youth sees his teachers as enemies, he interprets his teacher's encouragement as manipulating him or trying to make him look silly in front of his friends. Before his negative behavior can change, his view of reality must change.

We worked with one student who had been expelled from junior high and was constantly being suspended from the alternative school for fighting. This school was his last hope, and he was failing there. He had grown up in the projects in a family where everyone had to fight for everything they got, which wasn't much. He reacted so quickly that he could deck another student or teacher before they even knew they were in a fight.

Our social worker built a rapport with the boy by showing him respect, by engaging him about his interests, by kidding around with him, and showing that he liked him, despite his problem behavior. Over the weeks, as the student listened to the counselor talk about moods, habits of thinking, and self-esteem, he started to see that his knee-jerk reactiveness was self-defeating. As he noticed how his ego kept him in these patterns, his wisdom clicked into gear and revealed these habits in a new light.

As the boy's natural self-esteem and good feelings emerged, he started to see it as a challenge to stay out of fights, to walk away from potentially incendiary situations. He took it as an interesting experiment to get his teachers to change their bad opinion of him. And he started doing his homework.

The boy finished his last semester in junior high with a B average and conduct grades high enough to qualify him for the regular high school. He is now doing well in high school and plans to apply to college. He is not merely coping with his circumstances; he is managing his life.

Teaching Teens to Think for Themselves

Throughout our work, we found that young people are fascinated by the notion that their "reality" is determined by their own thinking. They want to know why different people think in so many different ways. They easily grasp how insecurity makes people cling to their self-concept. They can see how this idea connects with things like peer pressure and gangs. They recognize that the way people behave hinges on how seriously they take their own thoughts.

We tried to show them how they could use their common sense to make good decisions. We encouraged them to step back and look at things from a broader perspective, from the other person's shoes. We showed them how it feels to be reflective rather than reactive. In a gang intervention program done in Stockton, California, the youth were taught to question how they thought about things in knee jerk ways. They started to see that other youth like them weren't necessarily their mortal enemies just because they wore a different gang's colors. They started working together across gang membership to take on positive community projects.

In the self-esteem "rap" groups, our staff explained how people learn to attach certain thoughts to their self-esteem. We didn't try to force participants to change their outlook. Instead, we showed them that they could see things in different ways if they chose to, and that we respected them regardless of their choices and behavior. We always attempted to explain the link between thought and someone's outlook in an impersonal and entertaining way.

We didn't try to motivate the youth in our programs with threats or material incentives. We merely discussed what a common sense viewpoint entails and how it helps people deal with things with less upset and frustration. We found the best way to present ideas in the groups was to offer neutral observations without pushing ideas down their throats.

Within two semesters, we saw discipline referrals among these teens decrease by 75%. After one year their school failure rate dropped from 64% to less than 12%. After three years, the teen pregnancy rate plummeted by 80% at the junior high level. Many of these young people are now going on to college. In the past, most of them would have been in jail or dead before age 25. Many other youth are in vocational training and are working in legitimate jobs.

As the teenagers began to recognize their commonality, they recognized the unnecessary stress they were making for themselves when they emphasized their differences. They saw how their low moods and insecure thoughts kept them from appreciating each other and began to forge solid friendships across races and cultures.

Replicating These Results

In the time since we completed our initial intervention project in Dade County, we have implemented similar programs across the country and seen similarly positive outcomes. In data collected from Florida to Hawaii, grade point averages of at-risk students improved by 65%. Self-esteem scores rose from the 40th to the 80th percentile. Absenteeism and school discipline referrals dropped below national averages. Large community development corporations in places like the South Bronx are reporting that they are getting substantially more resident involvement in their programs, that staff are relating to residents, and to one another, in more positive, respectful ways and that family violence has already decreased noticeably.

The clients in these projects were at-risk youth, and parents. Most were exposed only to our parent groups, self-esteem classes or student rap groups. None were taught any specific problem-solving techniques or strategies. None received external reinforcements to modify behavior. None participated in support groups that analyzed their past experiences or taught that they were a product of their family history. And most reported that they felt better without trying.

As young people tapped into their innate resources for health, their newfound maturity and motivation affected other students, parents, and teachers in ways that gave the whole community a lift. Given that this pattern has proven to be replicable, these programs hold enormous promise for tackling a host of social ills from crime and teen pregnancy to school failure and welfare dependence.

These results, and this model of community revitalization and prevention is now being written into national and state policy statements on addressing problems of welfare dependence and crime as well as problems like school failure, teen pregnancy, drugs, teen violence and alienation. As can be seen from the above examples, the Health Realization model has brought new hope to an arena where many well intentioned leaders have thrown up their hands.

In the following chapter, I will discuss how this model addresses problems of ordinary day to day stress in life as well as marital problems and other kinds of adjustment disorders. In Chapter Nine, I will attempt to show how this paradigm views serious mental illnesses and provides some hope for better solutions even in the arena of chronic and severe emotional disturbances.

CHAPTER EIGHT

Stress, Life Adjustment and Relationships

In the previous chapter I presented the applications of this health realization model of mental health to prevention and early intervention. I reviewed the outcomes of pilot programs with extremely high risk families and neighborhoods. In this chapter I will attempt to generalize these findings to what we would consider the more normal and pervasive pressures of daily life.

Problems of stress and adjustment to the daily pressures of modern life have affected many people adversely. Also problems in marriages, due to stress and other factors affecting today's relationships, are rampant in today's American way of life. Stress management, marital counseling and treatment for adjustment disorders have become a compelling focus for psychologists from coast to coast. It is worthwhile to explore the approach Psychology of Mind practitioners take to alleviating these problems. Finding more solid answers to these problems would make life easier and more rewarding for millions of Americans, and most probably, would spill over to impact other facets of society.

Many people blame failed marriages on a lack of compatibility. Others say that they grew away from their partner or fell out of love. In Chapter Three we discussed how personality and personal likes and dislikes stem from people's conditioned separate realities. Most marital difficulties stem from this same root cause. It is a fairly obvious psychological fact that each partner has a separate reality. Each person's reality is composed of whatever they learned growing up. At different times, as we discussed earlier, people are more or less attached to their separate, learned reality. When one partner feels insecure, anything the other partner views differently is seen as a threat to their well being, and at times, even their survival.

A somewhat humorous, but instructive, example of this dynamic involved a woman from Jamaica who was in graduate school to get her masters in counseling. During a class discussion of separate realities, she related a story of her first marriage. She had grown up in a wealthy, conservative family in Jamaica. Up until her marriage she had never seen a man without his pajamas, including her father, brothers and so-on. On her wedding night, her new husband walked out of the bathroom naked. She was so shocked and upset that she immediately got dressed and went to the airport to fly home to her parents. The marriage was never revived after that incident.

This may seem extreme but most fights or disagreements in relationships are of this ilk. We have seen couples on the verge of divorce over whether one is a "slob" or the other an obsessive compulsive "neat freak." When people recognize these are different habits of thought, they move their differences outside the framework of right and wrong. Using common sense, they can then see that each has something to contribute to an entirely new view of things; to finding a way that both can not only live with but perhaps even enjoy, since it is something new for both people. We are starting to see that understanding the role of thought in relationships can bring once loving relationships back to life. We certainly found that over and over again with the parents and youth who participated in our prevention-early intervention programs.

Thought And Relationships

Since everyone has developed different habits, likes and dislikes, different opinions and attitudes, no two people will ever see things exactly alike. When couples start out together this isn't important to them. Why? They are in love. Once they have been together for awhile, they start to be exposed to each others habits and quirks. If they are tired or in a bad mood or feeling a little insecure, they will tend to take their differences more personally.

When this happens feelings of annoyance and irritation, or defensiveness and feeling misunderstood begin to compete with their love and affectionate feelings. The more insecure they become, the more wedded they are to their own beliefs. The more threatened they will feel when their partner does things differently or does not grasp how they think they should be treated by their partner. In the absence of understanding where these differences originate, each person will tend to hang on to their resentments and let them fester or build up. In some cases these feelings start to be the "normal," expected feelings prevailing in that relationship.

We have found over and over that relationships succeed not because people are compatible in their interests or likes and dislikes. The most successful relationships are those where people have enough wisdom to navigate their own thoughts and moods without blaming the other person. This kind of navigating is guided by the channel markers of recognizing the nature of separate realities and the role of thought in daily life.

In relationships we can see that people get upset and combative to the extent that they take their view of things too seriously. When we look at the dynamics of stress, we notice that different people can take on different amounts of stress from the same circumstances. In both instances the common denominator is how each of them holds their situation in their thinking, how seriously they take their conditioned view of that reality.

Is Stress a Given in Life?

Over many years, psychologists held that certain events caused predictable amounts of stress, for anyone. They did studies to measure the amount of stress connected to different events. For example, getting divorced, fired, or losing a parent were worth a certain number of points on the standardized stress scale. So were positive occurrences such as getting married, starting a new job, or having a baby.

During a training we conducted for psychiatric staff at the V.A. Hospital in Miami, a nationally known speaker explained how to calculate points on his stress scale. One participant, a psychologist who had recently graduated, moved to Miami from

Virginia, gotten married, and started a new job added up his stress points. He was surprised to find himself so far off the scale that by all rights he should have been a hospital patient instead of a staff member! Yet he felt that overall, he was reasonably calm and happy.

His responses to supposedly stress producing situations were unique to him. So are everyone else's. Also people respond differently to stress at different times, depending on their state of mind. What we have learned, and what we observe daily, is that every person perceives and experiences the same situation very differently. A situation that is stressful to one could be seen as a challenge, or merely shrugged off, by another. The variable that determines what the response will be is thought.

Conditioned Thought is the Villain in These Situations.

I once had a friend who loved to ski; being a good skier was a big part of who he thought he was. As he was driving to a ski area with his family and his best friend, his van overheated. He sat on the mountain road, exasperated as he waited for a passing car to give him a lift to a service station. In the meantime, his friend started a snowball fight with the children. As they laughed and played in the snow, my friend was furious at them for not being as upset as he was about getting such a late start on the slopes. By judging his companions and his situation as flawed because they didn't meet his expectations, he subjected himself to stress of his own making, and it made him miserable.

Stress and discord in relationships can usually be traced back to thought. Stress too is traceable to thought; thought in the form of learned expectations or our self image. Just consider. We all know single people who constantly fret about finding a partner and other singles who enjoy life as it is. Ironically, the latter group have more lasting and rewarding relationships when they do pair up with someone. Some middle managers are proud of how far they've come, while others despair at missing the executive suite and take their frustration out on their subordinates and families. The only difference between degrees of contentment and stress in these situations is thought.

People experience stress commensurate with the significance they attach to an event. While no one event delivers a predictable number of "stress points," the importance we accord an event in our thinking and the amount of stress we experience as a result is indeed predictable and measurable. In relationships the amount of conflict or discord is usually determined by how hard each partner is fighting to maintain their own view of reality. This observation holds up even in couples with whom we have worked who are in abusive relationships. Either each partner does not see how much they are contributing to getting the other riled up, or they have a view of who their partner is and what is happening that is way off the reality of what was really happening. Each of these viewpoints contributes to maintaining the status quo.

We worked with women in abusive relationships, for example, who felt that their man beating on them meant that he loved them. They were more worried when they were being ignored. Others believed that they were at fault or that things would get better, flying in the face of the evidence that it wasn't getting better. In other cases, one person's self concept may cause them to not want to change things. They may not want to be the one to rock the boat, or to give up on the marriage.

Relationships, Stress and Self-image

Stress, like beauty, is in the eye of the beholder. How another person looks to us in any relationship is also in the eye of the beholder. Much of our discomfort stems from the learned need to maintain a self-image based on what we think we need to be happy, to feel good about ourselves and others. In Chapter Three I introduced the idea that much of our personality that gets us in trouble in life is really a self image, held in place by thought. Because society in general teaches that the quality of our life is determined by external criteria, we have learned to make a lot out of how we feel that we should be treated by others. This bad habit is one of the biggest barriers to happiness and stability in relationships.

American society tends to support the notion that our accomplishments define who we are. Parents often teach their children that their worth depends on where they go to college, how much money they make, who they know, the color of their skin, their athletic ability, and so on. We think we're helping them by instilling the drive to succeed. In fact, though, we are condemning them to a life where stress comes with the territory. As parents and as a society, we pass these habits of thought, and the stress that results, across generations, races, and cultures. We don't mean to create harm, but do it innocently anyway.

At one time or another, all of us are affected by the feelings of insecurity and stress that come with trying to prove that we are who we want to think we are. This pattern is so widespread that striving, worrying and defensiveness often feel like our only choice, like second nature. One of the conclusions we are beginning to reach, in our work, is that stress is normal but not necessarily natural or inevitable. It seems to be mostly a function of how deeply a person realizes the role of thought in determining their experience of stress.

I once worked with a newspaper editor, for example, who had come for assistance because his experience of writing editorials was stressful. He put it off as long as he could, he worried and spent sleepless nights concerned about how well he could do it. We talked about why he had gone into writing. It was because he loved writing short stories and being a reporter on the school paper. We talked about how he had done better on papers in college when he wasn't as concerned about his grade, but more intensely interested in the material. He recognized that being worried about how he was doing as a professional was an ingrained habit of thought he had made important. He approached his next editorial assignment with the kind of enthusiasm and curiosity he had felt when he first began investigative reporting. He found the product was better and he loved the process of writing it. He started to feel engaged and challenged by his job in a much nicer way for his stress level.

These kinds of examples may seem like pie in the sky stories or unusual exceptions to the norm. But in fact, our first nature is unconditional self-worth. From our work in extremely hard core situations, with people in the criminal justice system, and in extremely disadvantaged circumstances, we would argue now that everyone has at least the potential capability to enjoy their life, to appreciate what they have and to live with common sense. In this arena, the exceptions prove the rule. Every once in a while we hear of someone who had started a new life as an artist, a writer, a performer or some other career while in prison. We hear of people who transcended life in a concentration camp. We hear of people who found they were terminally ill and became more peaceful, inspired and joyous people. Often we assign them the label of being exceptional human beings, of finding a resiliency or a spirit that few have within them.

From our findings, we would say now that these are attributes which everyone has, in full measure always within them. Too often people find them again only after they have given up on trying to find happiness from outside. Children are born with these attributes. Older people, after the prime of their life sometimes regain access to these qualities. Perhaps because they have grown tired of, or moved beyond, trying to prove themselves in life. In spite of our efforts, and those of other researchers in the prevention field, we have not seen any factors that tell us there are resilient people and those who are non-resilient.

In practice, this means someone can fully enjoy what they are doing, whether or not anybody else thinks it is worthwhile. When a young child sets aside an expensive toy to play with the box it came in, she doesn't feel the need to justify her choice to others, does she? Yet as she grows up she may start to get the message from her friends or parents that it isn't cool, and that she needs to go for the expensive gifts or possessions.

The Benefits of Noncontingent Self-worth

Thanks to our culture's tradition of attaching self importance to accomplishment, the counseling profession currently is engaged in lively debate over the true nature of self-esteem. Some argue that the need to prove ourselves and accomplish is innate and that people can only define themselves in this way. This view has led to a proliferation of techniques for building up a person's "ego-strengths." Others feel that if people begin to actually like themselves the way they are, they will become lazy and be underachievers. They might not be motivated to improve themselves or accomplish anything worthwhile.

Our experience with clients in all walks of life over the last fifteen years has been just the opposite. As we discussed in our chapter on prevention, good feelings and a lack of self consciousness open up the door to other capacities. These include mature judgment, creativity, insight and intrinsic, self motivation. People begin to do better for the personal satisfaction of doing something well. They learn for the sheer joy of learning.

Let me explain with an example from my profession. As I saw my colleagues begin to enjoy more noncontingent self-esteem, I noticed as well that they were less into the politics of their profession, and less worried about their standing in the eyes of their colleagues. At the same time, they exhibited heightened creativity and productivity, not complacency. With no marked intellectual advantage, they are producing work on the cutting edge of the profession, probably because they can open themselves to the lesson in every experience in a way that never happens when you are functioning from the image of self importance that we would call the ego.

The stress that arises from feeling the need to achieve in order to prove ourselves always dulls our mental clarity. I know a young man who received an athletic scholarship to a well-known liberal arts college, which asked him to complete a year of prep school to prepare him for his academic course work. He enrolled with some trepidation, but was instantly engaged by instructors who seemed fascinated with what they were teaching. For the first time in his life, he really enjoyed his academic work. His grade point average reflected his enthusiasm, and landed him on the dean's list.

Instantly, he began to worry about how he would maintain this high level of performance. By attaching his self-image to his academic performance and pouring on the pressure, he stopped having fun in class and found it harder to study, with predictably unfortunate results.

Along similar lines, many entertainment and sports stars have trouble avoiding getting their egos caught up in the adoring attention they receive from fans and the media. When fame draws their ego into the mix, they begin to take on stress from the pressure of feeling that they must constantly live up to their reputation, justify their immense salaries, and so forth. We have seen athletes and entertainers turn to drugs or alcohol to handle these pressures, or become extremely difficult to work with in a way that harms their careers.

The truly great athletes and stars are the ones who manage to somehow keep all this in perspective. They realize that their family life, their privacy and their enjoyment of life on their own terms is more important than the fickle public eye. Others become confused or arrogant, and begin to falter, lose their focus, or lose their drive. The worst of it, though, is losing the joyous flow of the talent and skill that made them great in the first place. They lose the inner satisfaction and excitement that come with unselfconscious immersion in the creative process. They lose the feelings that drew them into their craft and made them stars.

The insecurity and doubt that come with these kinds of pressures can lead to the problems we constantly see in the sports pages or the front pages of our newspapers. Spousal abuse, driving fast, fighting or failing drug tests are all constant parts of our diet when we read about the lives of many professional athletes. It would be nice for these athletes, who have contributed to other's lives through their talents, to enjoy a life of more contentment and to genuinely appreciate and benefit from their success in terms of the quality of their day to day lives.

Making Relationships Work Without Stress

Everything seems to go better when we are not thinking of ourselves in a self conscious way. Relationships get better with age when we accept both ourselves and the other person equally as we are. We then learn more all the time about both our partner and ourselves. The more we can stay out of our ego, the more we can see the other with compassion and affection. The more we stay in this feeling state, the easier it is to bring out the best in our partner. We cannot do this with fixed, rigid expectations.

Maintaining a set of beliefs about how our life should look, means forcing life to live up to our expectations. At times this effort can feel critically important to our well-being. It is actually a constant source of stress and insecurity. And as you've already seen, it doesn't matter if the self-concept is positive or negative. Having to live up to any externally imposed expectations generates as much anxiety as having to live within a prison of negative expectations.

In relationships, the closer and more intimate the relationship, the more it is a test of our ego and our ability to let go of our thinking, to let go of wanting to be right in order to learn how to be happy in that relationship. Particularly in close relationships we find that when we feel the need to fortify our self-image, or to justify and defend our opinions and expectations, everything gets harder. We add a layer of anxiety, conflict and effort to every interaction. In the classroom, these feelings make students distracted or alienated from learning. In organizations, it causes performance anxiety, lowers morale, and increases political wrangling. Ego always generates strife and misunderstanding instead of cooperation, respect, and supportiveness.

Insecurity is an inevitable by-product of attempting to live up to a set of learned standards. Insecurity makes adjusting to change and new situations more difficult. It helps greatly to recognize that insecurity is only the thought that our personal beliefs are important to our feelings of self worth. It makes us want to prove the other person wrong no matter what the cost. This thought is the glue that keeps us attached to all of our feelings of self consciousness in ways that cause stress. Insecurity is the dimension that keeps relationships at odds, producing conflict and misunderstanding

The least stressful frame of mind to be in is a state where we are not consciously aware of our self-image. In fact, we have the most self-esteem when we are least concerned about ourselves and the impressions we are making. The psychological perspective I would now associate with self-esteem, common sense, motivation, and enthusiasm for life returns when we forget about ourselves.

We all know how it feels to enjoy something so much that we lose ourselves in it. That's when we're the most creative, the most insightful, and motivated. All human beings have access to the state of mind where we lose ourselves, where we don't attach what we do to who we think we are. In relationships as well, we enjoy ourselves more and find the relationship more satisfying when we accept people on their own terms, and are interested in their world as opposed to needing to defend or justify our world.

When we are not self-conscious, the wisdom we access in that frame of mind shows us that it seldom makes sense to take things that others do personally. We see more clearly that everyone is basing their views on their learned ways of thinking about things. We can then be compassionate without feeling manipulated as we see that other people are insecure and are acting accordingly. In a less self-conscious state of mind, we are motivated by a desire to contribute, to solve the problem or improve the situation. And we have the clarity to see the best solution.

When we are not self-conscious, we see our mistakes not as failures but as learning experiences that will help us do better next time. We are less likely to feel overwhelmed or hopeless when things go wrong. Life teaches us at every moment when we are in a state of self-esteem. We are constantly growing and evolving in well-being and wisdom.

Stress and the Past

Many people carry resentment or guilt from the past into the present via thinking. As a result, they walk through their lives burdened by the stress associated with events gone by. When we continue to focus on what has been done to us or what we have done to others, we are still in the arena of self-concept. In our natural state of self-esteem, we can see that whatever we did or anyone else did to us, it was the best we could manage at the time. What a relief it is to just drop those burdens.

By dropping habitual negative thoughts from the past, by dropping habits of thinking that create resentment and frustration, we can reduce stress significantly and move into a psychological state where insight and wisdom click in and enrich our lives. Over and over again, my colleagues and I have seen clients experience this shift in perspective by dropping habits of thought that perpetuate stress. And we have seen their stressful feelings give way to feelings of gratitude, enthusiasm, appreciation, and love.

If society recognized and could acknowledge that stress may be normal, but it most definitely is not natural, fewer people would be caught up in the web of proving themselves constantly. And more people would understand the stressful consequences of envy, regret, and resentment, and see a clearer path to higher ground. They would most likely begin to see people with understanding across cultures. They would begin to recognize more how we are all alike rather than being stopped by our differences.

In the following chapter I will discuss how the principles of this paradigm have shifted our view of severe emotional disorders. We are beginning to recognize how these disorders are related to the ways that people take on stress, or operate out of a distorted view of things in ordinary day to day life. From making these connections we are feeling more hopeful that we can make progress in the treatment of these more severe disorders. In the final chapter, I will tie all of these ideas together and look at their implications for further research and the evolution theory in the field of psychology.

CHAPTER NINE

Potential Applications to Severe Disturbances

The literature in the field of psychology now tends to treat severe mental disorders as a different type of phenomena than adjustment disorders or ordinary problems of stress. One reason for this bias is that researchers have identified a biochemical component to these illnesses. Another reason has been that historically, people with these illnesses are unresponsive to normal forms of counseling or psychotherapy. Yet if we are to propose a paradigm that is explanatory of all psychological phenomena, this theory should also apply to extreme emotional disorders, including schizophrenia and other severe diagnoses, such as chemical dependency and affective disorders.

The view that these illnesses are completely different phenomena than our ordinary lives is compelling. A client moving in and out of extremely irrational states of mind to the point where they act in bizarre ways does not seem like us. While we all have ups and downs, our irrational thoughts when we are in an insecure state of mind are not as extreme as someone who is hallucinating or having paranoid delusional thought patterns. Still, we all have times when we are in more irrational states of mind and things look worse to us than they really are. Logically, a case could be made that the more severe emotional disorders produce extreme versions of insecure states of mind, at much further levels along this continuum.

Schizophrenia, in the language of the Diagnostic and Statistical Manual of Mental Disorders is defined as a thought disorder. The logic of the P.O.M. model would state that these severe disorders are characterized by thought systems that have gone out of control. As we discussed in the previous chapter, everyone's thoughts at times produce stress and less productive behavior. Given the extent to which people see things differently and the way people become attached to their beliefs, it would seem hard to understand why our thought systems don't get more out of control than they do.

While very few parts of the United States have to endure subzero temperatures, of minus 60+ degrees such as we find in Arctic regions, these extremes are still on the continuum of temperature gradients. We know what causes these extreme variations in weather across the globe. What is debatable is the cause of the extreme aberrations in someone's thoughts and perceptions that culminate in their being labeled schizophrenic, bipolar or extremely depressed. Our observations over the last fifteen years indicate that the more insecure someone is the more they misuse thought. In addition the more insecure people are, the less aware they are that what they are experiencing has anything to do with anything like thought.

A psychiatrist, who has worked with hospitalized clients now for over twelve years using this model, made some interesting observations on how chronic and severe illness stems from what seem like more ordinary fears, worries or concerns. In taking the histories of hundreds of clients he has noticed that the clients, prior to the onset of illness, were serious worriers or had mild anxiety attacks or were somewhat paranoid or hostile much of the time. He hypothesized that they were already fairly insecure people who had experienced a shift to a less stable state of mind. The shift was usually caused by the self validating nature of a thought system. Let us say that someone is relatively high in performance anxiety and also believes that they aren't attractive to the opposite sex. If this person breaks up with his girlfriend, for example, he may feel depressed because it validates his belief that he is unattractive. He also may fear not finding anyone else. This fear may cause him to isolate himself or feel awkward at the wrong times. When things don't look up, he gets a little more depressed and hopeless, which affects his work. When his boss comes down on him he gets severely anxious about his job performance. Most of us can see a downward spiral in the making.

The more depressed he becomes the more he isolates himself, and the more his work suffers. In this state of mind, he isn't fit for any relationship and is so anxious at work that his performance falls way off. He is told he will probably be laid off in the next round of cuts. He gets so depressed and anxious that he calls in sick a lot and just lays around feeling suicidal. He may start losing sleep because of his worry and anxiety. Such a downward spiral is understandable in this situation, and is fueled by thought. Yet it can culminate in a nervous breakdown, severe chronic depression or worse.

In this chapter I will attempt to offer this view from a perspective that allows for a biochemical element as well as a cognitive source. I will review our clinical experience with this client population over the last fifteen years. I will tie these observations into research carried out in ex-hospital aftercare and community based alternatives to hospitalization programs. I will do this in the context of realizing that these conclusions are highly preliminary, and indicate the need for more rigorous and in-depth research. There is mounting evidence for the consideration that the manifestations of mental illness could be learned coping responses to extremes of insecure, conditioned thinking.

Insecurity and Mental Illness

In this chapter I will attempt to show that there could be a logical link between insecurity and severe mental illness. When anyone gets insecure his imagination fills in the gaps and he sees things in an overly frightening way. We may imagine that our friends don't really care about us or that something bad will happen to us. We may feel discouraged or disillusioned about our life, feel that everything is hopeless and stay in bed all day. When our mental health comes back we may rebound and regain a more rational state of mind. We then realize that we have overreacted to things based on our insecure thoughts.

This behavior is not as irrational as the behavior of someone who is experiencing hallucinations, or having what psychology would call a psychotic episode. Yet it could be a matter of degree. Clients who are labeled as schizophrenic at times function in rational states of mind. In a doctoral dissertation recently completed on applications of Psychology of Mind to the treatment of schizophrenia, the research hypothesis was that when these clients become frightened their mind produces thoughts that are more extreme distortions of reality than us "normal" folks.

We have had clients, for example, who thought that their parents were poisoning their food, that their neighbors were spying on them, that the CIA or alien beings were after them, that the television was controlling their mind, that they talked to people who had passed away. These paranoid thoughts lead to what we observe as bizarre behavior patterns. Psychology of Mind would conclude that these thoughts are produced by that person's imagination in frightened states of mind. At these times they appear real to the person. Thought is still the link in the sense that hallucinations or paranoid states are produced by thoughts the person is having in those extremely insecure states of mind.

The Power of Our Thinking

When thought is linked with consciousness it is a very powerful thing. Society as a whole sometimes becomes gripped by extremely irrational, insecure thoughts. At one point we thought the earth was flat, and that if we went too far in one direction we would fall off the end of the earth. We once felt that people who behaved in certain ways were possessed by demons. We burned people at the stake for being witches. We can make ourselves extremely paranoid and afraid of other people who may have a different racial or ethnic background from our own. Many people are superstitious about certain things. Some claim to have seen Elvis at the mall. We are just beginning to recognize the power of the human mind to take any thought system and make it appear as reality.

What We Know About Mental Illness

We have already learned a great deal with respect to what works and what does not work with this patient population. Multiple interventions, including psychotropic medication, seem to be indicated when someone is in danger to themselves and others and is totally unaware that they are misusing their thinking to harm themselves or others. However it makes some logical sense that some part of a treatment regime could be along the lines of trying out ways of teaching patients about the role of thought.

The most prevalent form of treatment for more severe mental disorders today utilizes medication to balance the biochemical changes associated with these illnesses. The prevalence of this approach is based on the fact that this method has proven to alleviate the symptoms the most. Yet we know that changes in thought can produce biochemical changes in the body. Stress can create ulcers for example. When some people get anxious they have migraine headaches. Others get upset stomachs or heart irregularities. People get hotter and sweat more when they are anxious.

All of these are physical changes originating from a change in thought. In any of these instances, the physical symptoms can increase the person's level of anxiety or fear. This reaction can in turn cause the physical symptoms to worsen. Medication can alleviate the physical symptoms and help the person feel that something is being done to help. They may then, at least temporarily, move into a more relaxed frame of mind, and not produce the same amount of paranoid or anxious thoughts. There is also evidence that psychotropic medications impact the signals in the brain that physiologically trigger certain patterns of thought. While they may not eliminate this programming, they cause it to be less likely that it will be accessed while on the neuroleptic medication.

There is some danger inherent in assigning immutable physical cause to mental illness. If we merely look at the impact of our imagination and the power of the placebo effect we recognize the danger of this trend. The media today are fascinated by multiple personalities. We take them seriously enough to ask the person who (which personality) we are talking to at any moment. I would say that at this point we are not helping the person. We may find ourselves acting as if there really are ten different folks in there. If we as experts are reinforcing what they are seeing, giving credence to what their imagination is making up as a reality independent of their thinking, we are inadvertently fostering the clients confusion as well as their fears that these things may actually be happening to them.

What we want to help them realize is that they are making all these people up. At least, even if they are unable to take charge of their thinking, they will understand better what is occurring. Our experience over the years with these clients has been that when they start to recognize the role of thought in this process, they do then start to function more of the time in rational states of mind. The hardest aspect of this teaching, for patients with severe mental illnesses, is to assist them in even considering the possibility that these experiences are a product of their thinking. The foremost difficulty is that they tend to become more insecure if there is any focus on their perceptions or on their behavior as being irrational.

The Link of Abnormal Behavior and Insecurity

From reviewing our clinical experiences we have observed that patients who present with severe emotional disorders have several things in common that could help explain habitual and extreme patterns of insecure thinking. First they all grew up in homes with very high levels of stress and reactivity. Parents often were themselves unstable or unhappy and, more often than not, dealt with things in an overly emotionally charged way. They tended to be judgmental and blaming and to fly off the handle as a way of dealing with their children and other aspects of their lives.

Most of the clients we saw also had displayed vivid imaginations at an early age. Many had been fans of science fiction or fantasy stories as youth. It appeared that they had gone deeper than others into their imagination, maybe to escape from how they perceived their family. Most had a history of being withdrawn and shy in school and exhibiting other signs of insecurity, prior to the onset of schizophrenia.

We also noticed that patients who were more emotionally unstable than others shifted from one reality to another abruptly. This happened so rapidly that they had no perspective on what was happening. They would be completely immersed in one reality and then suddenly they were just as immersed in another. In some people we call this radical changing of realities multiple personalities, or bipolar (manic-depressive). In others we call it schizophrenia. Compared to these clients, most of us would experience our mood shifts as occurring in slow motion relative to what these people experience.

Addressing Insecurity in Treatment

We have found in our clinical work with this population that if we are able to calm people down, they tend to return to a more common sense state of mind. This argues for the point that mental health has a buoyancy, even in people with severe emotional disorders. If they can slow down their thinking, their rational perspective returns. When the patients can see for themselves that this works, they are able to calm themselves down more often. Their more rational states of mind then should gradually become more frequent and their behavior more stable.

These observations are somewhat reinforced by a research review carried out on the experience of community based rehabilitation programs in the seventies and eighties. During the mid nineteen eighties I worked as a consultant to a state agency that was responsible for de-institutionalizing hospitalized mental patients. Almost every state at this time was experimenting with programs that would work to stabilize these patients in the community. I was asked to make recommendations regarding the design of after care, residential and day treatment programs.

In preparing our recommendations to the State Department of Mental Health, we reviewed a great deal of the literature on psychiatric rehabilitation. We looked at what had been tried in other states and countries. This research had come up with some interesting observations that showed a predictable pattern of behavior in response to stress on the part of psychiatric patients. The data demonstrated that patients tended to have psychotic breaks or relapse when they were around people who were themselves emotionally reactive. In other words if the people around the clients became upset or anxious the client would interpret these reactions in a way that frightened them or made them feel insecure. They would then retreat into their own imagination to make up reasons for this fear.

As clients became more and more insecure they would make up a version of what was causing that fear that was much more exaggerated than the reality of the people around them. The extreme nature of their reaction would make the people around them more upset or nervous. The client would react to this by thinking and acting in even more bizarre ways. Soon they would be out of control and headed for a relapse. In programs where staff were trained to stay calm and were able to not react to the clients symptoms they were able to sustain lower relapse rates. Staff were even more successful if they were able to consistently treat their clients as capable of being healthy and reassure them when they began to feel frightened.

Probably because of the tradition in psychiatry that views mental illness as trait related, the researchers in these studies interpreted these findings as showing that psychiatric patients had a core psychological deficit. This character or genetic deficit supposedly caused them to overact to stress or emotional upset and to emotional expressiveness in their environment. However, with our patients it seemed much more helpful to see it as a state of mind change to an extremely insecure frame of reference. Rehabilitation programs based on this premise showed more success than others. They found generally that programs which were aimed at maximizing health, that focused on the person's capabilities and competence worked better in practice than programs aimed primarily at symptom reduction. In other words, programs worked better if they treated the person as having a capacity for health, while minimizing their attention to symptoms.

The Potential of Health Realization

These studies were useful as they were done in settings where patients could not be physically restrained. Still the after care or de-institutionalization program was being paid to keep them out of the hospital. Their goals were to keep patients functioning semi-independently, at least, in the community. In almost every setting these agencies found that traditional psychotherapy had either no measurable effect, or had an adverse affect. One reason was that patients became insecure if asked to talk about their past, to self disclose or express emotions.

One study stated that "a well known axiom of rehabilitation is that minimizing or suppressing sickness will not automatically lead toward improvement in functional capacity." Programs quickly moved toward a competency and skill building focus. Staff working in these programs became eclectic, looking around for whatever worked, rather than being wedded to any one treatment modality.

They found for example, that teaching worked better than analysis. Much of this teaching was aimed at helping clients understand the notion of intrinsic motivation, as a replacement for reliance on extrinsic rewards or to being so sensitive to the approval of others. They found, when teaching basic daily living skills, the client would generalize the common sense behind these skills if they discussed the principles underlying the specific skills being taught (including problem solving skills). They also found it helped to have clients do their own self evaluations and to actively involve them in setting goals and strategies to achieve their goals. All of these directions are consistent with Psychology of Mind principles and program design criteria. Yet these programs arrived at these methods through trial and error.

All of these characteristics of more successful programs relied on the clients ability to use their common sense, to calm down and put things in a more rational perspective. Most studies concluded that the less focus on the illness or pathology the better. In the write-up of one study, the researchers gave an example of what they called "paying attention to patient's strengths rather than spending time on their pathology:"

> Mary got a job as a maid in a hotel. A worker spent two days working side by side with her until she mastered the skills of the job. Two days later the worker received a call from Mary. She asked to go back to the

> hospital as the televisions in the rooms were controlling her brain and telling her what to do. The worker asked if something had happened that upset her earlier. She admitted that she had been told by her supervisor, in an impatient tone, that she was making the beds incorrectly. The worker came back and worked with her on making up the beds the way the supervisor wanted. She didn't even mention the symptoms that had emerged when the patient was feeling insecure. As soon as she knew what to do, she felt more secure in her job. The voices from the television went away. The worker also pointed out to Mary that it was a sure sign of health that she realized she needed help when she began to experience the television talking to her.

Other studies concluded that relating to clients as responsible citizens was an "extremely important" attitude for staff to adopt in order to work successfully with clients in the community. One study done through the University of Wisconsin is intriguing in this respect. It had followed an experimental group of hospitalized patients with diagnoses of chronic schizophrenia who participated in a health promotion model of aftercare.

These patients were moved into group apartments outside the hospital. Their only support was a social worker who taught them how to pay rent, budget their money, shop and do other practical tasks of daily life. The staff also told everybody in the client's immediate environment, including local shopkeepers, their landlords, family, friends and others, to consistently treat them as mature responsible people who could use common sense and make their own decisions. They were trained to not react to symptoms unless the person became dangerous to themselves or others.

The patients in this experimental group had a relapse rate that was almost two thirds less than the control groups treated with more traditional forms of therapy. A greater majority also went on to function better in jobs outside of sheltered workshop settings. The interesting aspect of this study was that the patients were not taught directly that they were healthy, but were consistently treated as if they were healthy. It would be interesting to see if outcomes would improve further if patients had been taught that they had a healthy side. What could have happened if they knew that this aspect of their functioning could override their pathology? The patients may have done even better.

These kinds of findings illustrate the potential of the application of Psychology of Mind to treating severe emotional disorders. We are not saying that we have all the answers to treatment in this arena. There have been fewer follow up studies done and fewer interventions designed for this patient population using Psychology of Mind than in the area of prevention or other types of therapy. We have not developed enough experience to attempt to define a specific treatment regime or to produce a tested methodology.

Our experience to date, corroborated by the psychiatric rehabilitation research, has been that working with this population with any modality is much more difficult. There is a tendency for patients to react adversely even to personal observations or to any kind of direct focus on their psychological functioning. Patients don't stay on their medication and may argue that the doctor is poisoning them. However, psychiatrists who have been using this approach in inpatient hospital settings and in their outpatient practices are reporting promising improvements in outcomes.

These observations tend to be confounded by the fact that many of these patients are also using psychotropic medications, and may have also had other forms of treatment. Yet even the programs I have visited around the country that emphasize promoting health as their key modality, see serious and permanent limitations in their clients. Most openly admit that they operate on the assumption that the chronicity of the illness is such that people will remain dependent to some degree on the mental health system for life. This assumption is communicated to the patient in ways that are intended for them to accept they have definite limitations on their capacity for health.

Does Promoting Health Put Patients at Risk?

Some groups of professionals have reacted to the premise that these clients have the same base of health as anyone with the fear that the patient will be allowed to go out on their own, will relapse when there is no support and end up in serious trouble. We would not disagree that people suffering more severe emotional disorders are in need of more supervision and patience. We would certainly recommend a gradual approach with an emphasis on incremental changes. The idea of most after care programs now is to wean people slowly away from dependence to whatever extent possible.

We found that it did take a great deal more tolerance and understanding to work with this client population. We had to learn to not react to behavior that could be frightening while insuring that the patient was not putting themselves or the people around them in any jeopardy. We had to learn to provide limits without losing our respect for the person and for their capacity for healthy functioning. We had to learn to not become discouraged by relapses but to see how to use them as learning experiences for both us and for the client.

Shifting the Focus of the Therapist

Many of our colleagues started to see their patients more like themselves. They recognized their patient's behavior as extreme versions of what they did when they were feeling insecure. They noted that this perspective helped. They could relate to and understand what the patient was going through in a way that made it less frightening and gave them a handle on how to help. Most started to pay less attention to the times when patients brought up their less rational perceptions. They learned to almost completely ignore these thoughts and change the subject to one where the patient could maintain a more rational perspective. (Usually something less charged and personal). They learned how to do this without losing the feeling of respect for the person.

They started noticing that sometimes a nice, friendly, saner conversation about trivial things, (movies, shopping, sports, recreational activities) gave their patient more of a feel for their capacity for health than an entire session spent analyzing the paranoid thoughts of the person, or trying to figure out where they came from and what they did or didn't mean. Patients seemed reassured that they could be healthy and that they did not need to rely as much on their craziness as a way of coping with what often seemed to them to be a hostile world.

Parents and friends or significant others in the lives of these patients were encouraged to go out an do more ordinary things with the patients. They were taught not to react to symptoms, but to remain calm and reassuring and respond as if nothing too serious had happened. Many of these patients were able to go back to work, or to school, or to significantly reduce both the incidence and severity of relapse over the time we were able to follow their progress.

It is always a judgment call to say whether someone is ready to take more responsibility or needs support at any time. It can usually only be accurately assessed in the moment when we recognize how the client is doing. The line between fostering health and fostering dependency can be hard to maintain sight of at times. Taking responsibility for clients versus setting appropriate limits can be fuzzy. Some researchers in the rehabilitation field note that many of their patients used their illness as an excuse for irresponsible behavior, including things like shoplifting and disrobing in public. They found that having natural consequences be a part of their lives like everyone else, helped. Patients could rationally grasp these consequences if staff helped them understand that this is just the way society works. Realizing that these consequences were not personal, not aimed at them, helped to change their chronic habits of taking things personally to the point of always feeling insecure.

Implications and Research Needs

Psychiatrists using P.O.M. found was that they were able to gradually reduce medication dosages and move their patients toward more independent functioning. Patients began to function better once they began to understand shifts in their thinking, from more to less insecure, as the cause of their abrupt shifts in states of mind. Even in paranoid or psychotic states they were able to stay more functional if they knew that these experiences came from their imagination rather than that these things were actually occurring.

One of the difficulties encountered when working with this population has been helping them stay in secure states of mind long enough to learn something about their thinking that would help them when they became upset or were moving toward a psychotic state. We found that this involved a lot of training of caretakers whether they were professionals, relatives or other staff who interacted with patients. These people needed to be trained in Psychology of Mind and apply it to themselves. They were then able to minimize their reactions to symptoms and continue to interact with the healthy side of the client.

A therapist in California whose caseload is primarily dual diagnosed clients, (e.g. chemical dependency and schizophrenia) has shared case studies with me over the last two years. Several of these stand out, in terms of the outcomes she was able to accomplish. One client is a 44 year old male who was diagnosed as schizophrenic at age 19. Since that time he has been continually in and out of either mental institutions or jail.

She began seeing him two and a half years prior to her report. He had been abusing both alcohol and crack. Hospital reports noted that he was often delusional. He reported that his neighbor was tormenting him and feared she was going to attack him. He lived with his mother, but they fought constantly. She reported that his delusions made him hard to manage.

The therapist helped him step back and consider the idea that everyone is doing their best and that people were not picking on him. Teachers who he thought had picked on him when he was younger he began to see were just doing their job the way they interpreted it. He started to have more compassion for them and for himself in that situation. He saw his neighbor as less threatening and gained compassion for the fact that she sometimes reacted to him with fear or suspicion. He began to see it as understandable.

He is now able to share his mother's home with her more peacefully. He began to let things go and understand the idea of "water off a duck's back" which helps him take things less personally. He feels certain that he will never be hospitalized again. He states that he knows he is in charge of his thinking process. He has a girlfriend, of five months, and is learning to cook and manage his own finances. He is exploring job and educational opportunities. His therapist reports that he is "walking differently, he laughs easily and is enjoying life more all the time."

One dual diagnosed client (affective disorder-chemical dependency) had attempted suicide three times in a ten year period and had been in and out of treatment for depression and chemical abuse for over 20 years. In the last three years, during treatment with this therapist, she has not considered suicide and has had no relapses. She reports she no longer has nightmares and understands the part her thinking plays in her feelings of self worth. A third client, hospitalized twice last year, exhibited paranoid reactions, hallucinations and depression. After eight months with this therapist, she reports that "he has gained control over his obsessive thinking, acceptance of his mood changes, and understands the difference between a mountain and a molehill. He is stable in recovery."

These clients calmed down, responding to being treated as if they were capable of being healthy. They stayed in rational states of mind more of the time while in therapy. During these periods they could understand that people sometimes get caught up in insecure thinking to an extent that causes them to lose perspective or to lose their grasp on what is their imagination and what is real.

There are a growing number of case studies of clients diagnosed as schizophrenic or who have been dual diagnosed. These patients have responded to this approach. Many learned that the world was not a crazy place, that it was safer than they thought when they became insecure. They used this knowledge to calm themselves down and regain their equilibrium when they started to get frightened and think in bizarre ways.

Researching the Potential of a New Focus of Treatment

There are patients of course who presented for treatment and were not significantly helped by applying this approach. Yet a number have been able to function in ways that are more independent than others would have given them credit for being able to accomplish. These outcomes point to the potential for Psychology of Mind to contribute to improved results in the treatment of severe disturbances. Such an advance will require research trials with this population under controlled conditions. A specific treatment methodology still needs to be developed and refined that will target the needs of this patient group. Such a modality should be tailored to the ways this group learns best, and to the levels of functioning at which this group is starting out. We feel that research and pilot programs in this area are a high priority.

Progress on this front could alleviate a great deal of suffering. We had a letter from a parent of one of our clients in Miami three years after he first came in to our clinic. He had been able to hold a job and go back to college. This parent said she would always be grateful that she had the opportunity to have a normal son. She indicated that she had been told by a number of psychiatrists that this was an impossibility.

If the premise is true that this client group has equal access to mental health, that they have the same core of health as anyone else, the potential for this kind of outcome is always a possibility. As responsible professionals we should be able to maintain the support required while continuing to nurture the clients healthy side to its fullest. More research is also obviously needed on the link of biochemical imbalances to the thought process. Yet, based on the promise that this approach holds for helping this population, we feel that this treatment modality should be adequately tested and assessed for its potential in assisting patients with severe and chronic disorder find the ability to lead a more normal life.

CHAPTER TEN

The Potential for a Renaissance in Psychology

A renaissance refers to a period of time when fresh thinking, new ideas and inventions spur society to advance the quality of human life in some way. These advances alleviate negative conditions or improve the circumstances under which people live. They are usually accompanied by new thinking in a variety of areas that contributes to advances in those fields.

It is time for a renaissance triggered by new thinking in the field of psychology. Psychology is a core science. It is a key science because how people think, how they feel and behave impacts all areas of life. Discoveries in psychology can lead to advances in all areas of human relations, social relations and human endeavors. Alleviating stress in society would impact the health of families, communities and the work place. More successfully addressing chronic mental illness would save millions in health care costs and help make productive many of those people who are now burdens to society. Advances in psychology can provide more effective answers to problems of deviance, crime, drugs and other social pathologies that plague our society. Genuine advances in our understanding of the mind would help us see ways to be more effective in eliminating prejudice, misunderstanding, fear and hate across cultures and ethnic groups. With such advances we can better resolve problems of motivation, morale, job satisfaction and interpersonal conflicts that adversely affect organizational functioning.

Vaclov Havel, the president of the Czech Republic was awarded the Philadelphia Liberty Medal on July Fourth, 1994 for his contributions to peace in Eastern Europe. In his acceptance speech, he noted that "the relationship to the world that modern science fostered and shaped appears to have exhausted its potential. The relationship is missing something. It fails to connect with the most intrinsic nature of reality and with natural human experience" (New York Times, Week in Review, July 08,

1994). The evolution of psychology as a science that provides us with a better understanding of human nature and human psychological functioning would provide a big part of what Havel eloquently notes is missing in our understanding of the human experience.

In this book, I have covered the early findings that led to the insights and principles we are calling Psychology of Mind. I reviewed the implications of these principles for the role and health of the helper. I explored their implications for therapy, for prevention, for mitigating stress, improving relationships and healing adjustment disorders. I looked at their potential for treating more severe disorders. After reviewing the results of these applications, many of us in the field of mental health are hopeful that this new paradigm can provide workable solutions to many of our most intransigent human problems.

In 1993 the Chancellor and Vice President for Institutional Advancement of a nationally known graduate school in psychology paid a site visit to the public housing intervention programs we initiated in Miami in 1987. They interviewed residents, welfare workers, the police chief and officers assigned to the projects. They also interviewed school personnel, counsellors, outreach workers and youth program workers. When asked what the major benefit of P.O.M. had been to their work, each stated that it was the practicality of this approach that was the most helpful. The interviewees testified that they were able to see ways to use this approach in every client contact or community situation, as well as with their co-workers and colleagues. In similar site visits to large scale community revitalization programs in the Bronx, the evaluators were told that the agencies involved in the training saw the practical benefits to the point that they trained staff at all levels within the organization, from the executive directors down to the building supers, as well as using it with the residents in their communities. It had payoffs in terms of management styles and interdepartmental cooperation as well as helping clients. It became clear to these investigators that this approach had demonstrated its effectiveness and its practical application in the most hard core settings.

Toward a Holistic, Practical Psychology

Not only has this approach demonstrated its practicality in settings where many professionals had written people off, it has also taken us back and reconnected us to the very foundations of modern psychology. Even prior to the existence of the field as a formalized body of knowledge, philosophers and scientists attempted to understand the human experience. From Socrates through Shakespeare, from the existentialists to the humanists, from Freud through Skinner human beings have tried to broaden and deepen our understanding of ourselves. This is a legitimate goal of psychology as well as philosophy. Now we are just beginning to see commonalities across all lines of inquiry that may help to accelerate our progress in understanding ourselves more fully.

When William James and William Wundt first began forming the field of psychology as a unique discipline, they sought a holistic understanding of the mind. James saw thought as a key underpinning of this understanding. As my colleagues and I began our journey, unraveling the implications of our early observations, we suspected that the ideas we happened on had the makings of a holistic understanding of human nature and human functioning. We were perhaps, headed back toward where psychology started. However, the earliest thinkers were more like philosophers and, as such, took less notice of the practical applications of their ideas. What excited us about our work was not only the broad implications of these ideas but also the practical value of their applications to both treatment and prevention.

The Evolution of Psychological Thought

Freud and his colleagues developed and refined the psychoanalytic model so that psychology would have practical tools to combat emotional distress. The attention of psychology was subsequently drawn to studying pathology, a subset of human behavior that was of primary interest to those schooled in the medical model. Since then psychologists and psychiatrists have identified more and more types of pathology. Since each category manifested with different symptoms, we began to develop specialized methods of treatment. These efforts to understand each type of illness separately has splintered the field, creating a focus on discrete categories of disturbance and methods of treatment. The field has also been influenced by competing schools of thought, becoming further categorized into different disorders, different etiologies and different cures. Not surprisingly, this direction has not led to a holistic psychology.

The Status of Psychology as a Science

The ongoing debate concerning whether psychology is yet a science is understandable. There is a lack of agreement within the field as to the most basic, underlying principles of cause and effect. Different schools of therapy have widely differing opinions; both of what the root causes are of emotional distress and mental illness and of what types of treatment provide solutions to these problems. However, there are recognizable trends within psychology that we can discern. In many ways, these trends dovetail with the findings reported in this book, all leading us in the direction of a more holistic understanding of operational principles that describe the workings of the human mind.

Psychoanalytic theory began with the idea that human nature was basically negative. Freud posited that the id, the most basic psychic force, was an animalistic drive for survival which, if left unchecked, would lead to destructive impulses. An unsocialized id would lead people to dominate, conquer, control, pillage and generally wreck havoc in life. Psychoanalytic theory posited that the id needed to be controlled by the ego and superego. The effectiveness of the ego (the adult, rational decision maker) and the superego (as a kind of personal conscience) was built up from the outside through socialization, upbringing, and from learning the values and morays of civilized society.

These early ideas initiated two major trends which have since permeated psychological theory. The first is that humans learn to be healthy, responsible adults from the outside in. The second is that people are a product of their past, and that at some point they become damaged goods with little chance of recovery to normal, healthy functioning.

With the advent of the behavioral schools in the 1950's and 60's, psychology moved toward viewing each person as a tabla rosa without intrinsic inclinations toward negativity or self destructive behavior. The behavioral schools viewed the psyche as a blank slate, with neither negative or positive predispositions. Everything we did, both positive and negative, was imprinted by external reinforcements and social or conditioned learning. People were seen as solely a product of their environment.

The field had shifted toward a more neutral view of human behavior. Yet the field retained the notion that behavior was learned from the outside in, and that people were a product of their past in a way that made change difficult or effortful. The cognitive schools made a major contribution when they introduced the idea that it was a person's thinking that is actually conditioned, not their behavior. However they still felt that people were a blank slate and that everyone's outlook, and thus every behavior, was learned from the outside environment.

With the cognitive breakthroughs, researchers had an inkling that defining the link of thought to perception would provide a new footing for how we perceive mental illness and social deviance, and how we do therapy. Yet the techniques adopted with clients were drawn from the previous behavioral models. Treatment remained focused on dealing with the problematic or dysfunctional aspects of thinking and behavior, attempting to reprogram the past imprinting new, more positive or functional beliefs and habits from outside-in.

Resiliency research, cited earlier in this book, suggests that human beings may actually be more than blank slates. We are now discovering what many of the humanistic schools suspected for centuries, that people have inner resources and a potential for higher order capacities that we, as yet, have not adequately accounted for in mainstream psychological theories. Yet the humanistic scholars never articulated a model that included everyday behavior along with the existence of higher order capacities. Such a model is necessary to turn humanist hunches into a practical psychology that would help substantially in the treatment and prevention of emotional disorders.

Psychology of Mind is an attempt to take the findings my colleagues and I, quite literally, stumbled onto in our research and make sense of them in this historical context. We are attempting to incorporate what we have learned about thought, mental health and resiliency in a way that makes the most sense, and complements how the field has developed, drawing conclusions then from this match.

When we began searching for the existence of basic principles to provide a foundation that would underlie a unifying theory, we focused on key phenomena that seemed to be universal, constants across individuals. We looked for dynamics that worked the same way for everyone regardless of circumstances, race, situation, socioeconomic status, background or learned ways of thinking.

Discovering The Indescribable

We observed that everyone continuously uses their thinking to evaluate their life. Thought constitutes the most basic fabric of life as it is experienced by human beings. The incredible mosaic of life that we observe across cultures, societies and subgroups within society is woven from this fabric of thought. For us as researchers, this seemed like a fertile direction in which to look for answers. The next logical question then seemed to be; exactly how do we weave this mosaic? What is the relationship of thought to consciousness? How does this process impact our everyday existence?

We realized that thought is a vehicle that acts as the intermediary connecting human beings to the external reality. The logic of this relationship is simple, but precise and constant, just like the logic of a mathematical formula. People's feelings and behavior are always consistent with their outlook, with how they perceive or interpret what is going on around them at the moment.

We also started to recognize the natural buoyancy of a "healthy" thought process. We saw clues concerning how insecure, self defeating thoughts are imprinted in the brain, both physiologically and from past experiences. Yet we also observed people in more relaxed states of mind accept themselves, feel better and be rational and objective, take things less personally and access common sense.

The process that governs the nature of resiliency, the immune system of the mind, is understandable, even at the most basic level. However, the state of natural mental immunity itself is difficult to describe. One of the major difficulties has been describing something that exists before we superimpose content, the thoughts that make up people's specific beliefs. Our explorations led us to a human state of mind that exists before thought. We found ourselves trying to describe a thought process that culminates in the contents of people's thinking. We saw a need to convey a psychological perspective we call mental health which, in essence, is content free. While wisdom and perspective help people make better choices, this perspective itself doesn't bring content to the table with it. While it enables us to view content (our past, our situation and our behavior) from a new vantage point, it is a mental perspective almost impossible to describe. It must be realized rather than memorized.

These discoveries, like any discovery concerning the fundamental nature of all phenomena, should provide us with more effective, targeted strategies for action. For example, in the mental health field advances should provide more effective methods of prevention and treatment. They have already given us a new direction and focus in our professional training and education programs.

The Nature of Reality and the Human Experience

As we started to get a better understanding of the role of thought, we realized that reality is indeed created from the inside out, not the other way around. We got a profound glimpse of how people create their reality moment to moment through thought. Fascinated, we wondered why this process

had not been more evident to us before that time. Even though we ourselves went in and out of different realities, ways of seeing things and levels of mental health, we had not recognized this fact. We did not realize that our fluctuating perceptions of reality were a function of our state of mind, not objective responses to circumstances.

We saw that one of the tasks of psychology would be to teach people not so much about their pasts, but about how reality is formed every minute from inside out via the gift of thought, a gift of human birthright. As the process of weaving life's infinite realities via thought became more apparent, we realized that most people functioned in life after the fact of their thinking, and within the framework of their learned beliefs. Most did not view their attitudes, opinions, values and perceptions as beliefs, but saw these beliefs as reality. Most of us are a part of the mosaic, not grasping many other worlds of beliefs that are being woven around us.

We now know that people do have a capacity for what the cognitive school of therapy has alluded to as meta-cognition, seeing facts about their own thinking. Humans can realize that they do have a set of beliefs which often colors their perceptions. We call this capacity a higher level of understanding because it is a higher level grasp of the nature of reality as well of their own psychological functioning. We saw people gain this understanding across cultures, many in spite of tremendous adversity in their lives.

The field of psychology itself was in the same boat as the rest of humanity. We psychological professionals had been functioning after the fact of thought, after the fact of our own thinking. Each school was using the basic capacity of thought to evaluate the same data in entirely different ways. Once again we were drawn back to a common denominator, thought, as the culprit coloring our interpretations.

We understood how this diversity of opinion could happen. When someone takes their thinking seriously, these thoughts become reality. They see the world in a way that provides evidence for the truth of that reality. In order to put psychology on a more objective scientific footing, we needed to look at something that was constant before these separate realities. Describing how thought and consciousness combine can logically explain the existence of all the separate realities that share "air time" in our society, across cultures, races and all external categories in which we put people.

Our findings were best explained by understanding the role of thought, the nature of resiliency and the existence of a healthy thought process. We realized how critically important it is for therapists to understand the role of thought for themselves. If we are the experts telling our clients what is or is not wrong with them, we must be careful about what we say. If we believe that they are a product of their past, they will also start to believe it. We may inadvertently teach our clients to see change as difficult. If we see life in a negative way, or think that the best people can do is learn to cope, then our clients feel similarly and often decide that the best they can do is cope with their disabilities in a hostile world. We must take responsibility for the thoughts we share with others, as they help to shape our client's realities.

Rethinking the Nature of Mental Health

We are beginning to see that mental health is more constant and more solid in human beings than mental illness. It also comes from inside out, not the other way around. It may be a somewhat radical proposition to suggest that mental health is a core state of being for everyone, a natural state, to which people cannot lose access. Yet, perhaps more than anything it has been most exciting for us to learn that mental health is much more than merely the absence of illness. It is, in and of itself, something that people can always get more of; they can deepen their well being, their ability for creativity and insight, their motivation and productivity, and their enjoyment of life more than we had previously thought possible.

Why had the field missed this fact? Perhaps because mental health is so natural and effortless that it is elusive in terms of definition and description. Perhaps because we focused our attention excessively on pathology. When we are physically healthy, we do not think much about our state of health. We take health for granted and go about our business until we get sick. Then we notice that our health is missing by its obvious absence, we don't feel good. Yet we also know that the body has its own resiliency and that we will eventually recover our health most of the time. The same dynamic holds true for our mental health. When we are not self conscious, we are involved fully in whatever we are doing. We are not analyzing our mental health. When we are upset or stressed and looking outside for the reason, we are not considering the possibility that this reality too is created from inside out, or that the mind has the resiliency to find a solution that brings back our mental health.

The medical field teaches that we can prevent illness by enhancing our bodies ability to fight disease, by increasing our level of health through exercise, diet, cutting down on habits such as drinking and smoking, and through strengthening our immune system. Mental health, we are discovering, works the same way. We can always find higher levels of self esteem, happiness and understanding. accessing greater degrees of mental health. Like exercising for physical health this provides an effective immunity for the prevention of most forms of mental illness.

Seeing the natural resiliency of mental health helps people recognize the futility of efforts by the intellect to find mental health. To realize the route to mental health, we had to learn to navigate around the minefield of our own thinking. Yet psychologists up to now have not assumed that mental health is something that is as free as the air around us or as natural as breathing. We had been looking at it as something that we had to put into people from outside rather than something we could help people find inside, and bring out.

In the P.O.M. model, our ability to think, to use free will to interpret life via thought is a constant. This ability is a basic fact of life concerning how we use the elements of the mind. Every human being has the use of these same elements, and uses the same kind of thought process. The mind will take whatever we are thinking and project it outward so that it takes on the appearance of reality. These psychological constants, or capacities exist in every person. How we use them is what varies across individuals. The job of the therapist is explaining how these elements work.

Therapy in this model emphasizes clients understanding that they have access to a healthy thought process, that they are capable of more than their thinking in stressful or insecure states of mind. Knowing the dynamics of their thought process enables them to take responsibility for, and strengthen their capacity for mental health. Until people are aware of the nature of their thought process, they cannot take responsibility for their behavior, even when they try. This is why our bad habits often seem so difficult to break. Behavior changes more easily and effortlessly when we recognize and reengage the healthy thought process.

From the principles presented, their applications and the outcome data offered in the previous chapters, the student may recognize that the principles of Psychology of Mind have implications for our view of human nature. Hopefully, this can be a more positive, inspiring view than some considered in the past.

The basic elements of Psychology of Mind can incorporate research across schools of thought within psychology. An understanding of these principles also helps clarify issues such as free will, choice and responsibility along with our relations to others in society.

The common denominator holding all of these things together is thought. Everything created by human beings started with a thought. A thought can be something learned in engineering graduate school about building bridges, or it can be a purely original thought. Original thoughts lead to new ideas and inventions for society. Cultures are created from thought. Robbing a bank or investing in the stock market stems from a thought. Behavior follows from the thought that makes the most sense to a person at the time.

In the P.O.M. model, mental well being and mental suffering both are creations of thought. My colleagues and I had to drop our notions of blame, judgement and right or wrong to recognize this. Like any scientist, we had to step outside of our learned ways of thinking to gain a more neutral perspective. In this book, I am asking for readers to do the same. It is not necessary to blindly accept, or to reactively disagree with these ideas. Consider the logic of this perspective. Does it intuitively make sense? Does the logic hold? Is it compelling? Could you see it applying to all kinds of behavior? To individual and collective behavior? To both healthy and unhealthy behavior?

If the answer to these questions is even a qualified yes, then we might have the beginnings of a new paradigm. As mentioned in preceding chapters, while P.O.M. practitioners have seen promising results, we feel that we are still at the beginning stages of fully understanding this paradigm. We are just beginning to realize the implications and understand the possible range of applications for this model.

One of our biggest challenges now is to carry out more rigorous research work in this area. Yet it is a challenge that my colleagues and I enthusiastically embrace. Personally, I can't think of any work I would rather do. We see the possibility of a renaissance not only for psychology, but for society. Imagine if people became aware of their healthy thought process? Imagine how that could help the world today. Imagine if human beings had perspective on their thinking? What would the impact be on societal tensions across races, ethnic groups and strata in society. Imagine if people could learn to think more creatively, without being stuck in their past? How much progress could we make in solving seemingly intransigent social ills. We are at the beginning of an exciting journey that will last well beyond our lifetime.

These ideas have now taken on a life of their own. Psychology of Mind has become a recognized school of thought in the mainstream of psychology. It is being used nationally and internationally to address problems of poverty, delinquency and alienation. It is increasingly being used in chemical dependency treatment centers and in mental hospitals and clinics with a variety of disorders. It is being researched and integrated into curriculum in major universities. It appears to be an idea whose time has come. I hope that this book has made these remarkable findings more understandable and more accessible to both lay readers and professionals in the mental health field. Lastly, I hope it has opened the doors of possibility more fully for you in your endeavors.

REFERENCES

Adams, E. H., Blanken, A. J., Ferguson, L. D., and Kopstein, A. 1990. *Overview of Selected Drug Trends*. Rockville, MD: National Institute on Drug Abuse.

Anthony, E., and Cohler, B. 1987. *The Invulnerable Child*. New York: Guilford Press.

Bailey, J. 1989. "New hope for depression: A study in neo-cognitive therapy" (Spring). Paper presented at the Eighth Annual Conference on Psychology of Mind, St. Petersburg, FL.

Bailey, J. 1990. *The Serenity Principle*. San Francisco: HarperandRow.

Bailey, J., Blevens, J. K., and Heath, C. 1988. "Early results: A six-year post-hoc follow-up study of the long term effectiveness of neo-cognitive psychotherapy." Paper presented at the Seventh Annual Psychology of Mind Conference, Coral Gables, FL.

Bandura, A. 1982. "Self-efficacy mechanism in human agency." *American Psychologist* 37: 122-147.

Bandura, A. 1989. "Human agency in social cognitive theory." *American Psychologists* 44: 1175-1184.

Bandura, J. 1990. "Self-regulation of motivation through anticipatory and self-reactive mechanisms." R. Dienstbier ed. Nebraska symposium on motivation: *Perspective On Motivation* 38: 69-164. Lincoln, NE: University of Nebraska Press.

Banks, S. 1985. *Second Chance*. New York: Fawcett Columbine.

Banks, S. 1989. *The Quest of the Pearl*. Tampa, FL: Duval-Bibb Publishing Co.

Baumrind, D. 1978. "Parental disciplinary patterns and social competence in children." *Youth and Society* 9: 239-276.

Baumrind, D. 1985. "Familial antecedents of adolescent drug use: A developmental perspective." *National Institute on Drug Abuse Research Monograph Service* 56: 13-44.

Beardelee, W., and Podorefsky, D. 1988. "Resilient adolescents whose parents have serious affective and other psychiatric disorders: Importance of self-understanding and relationships." *American Journal of Psychiatry* 145: 63-69.

Beck, A. T. 1976. "Cognitive therapy and the emotional disorders." New York: International Universities Press.

Benard, B. 1987. "Protective factor research: what we can learn from resilient children." *Illinois Prevention Forum* 7: 3-10.

Benard, B. 1991. *Fostering Resiliency in Kids: Protective factors in the family, school and communities*. San Francisco: Western Regional Center for Drug-Free Schools and Communities.

Benard, B. 1991. "Youth service: from youth as problems to youth as resources." *Illinois Prevention Forum* 10: 6-14.

Berlin, R., and Davis, R. 1989. "Children from alcoholic families: Vulnerability and resilience." T. Dugan and

R. Coles eds., *The Child in Our Times: Studies in the development of resiliency:* 81-105. New York: Brunner-Manzel.

Blais, G. 1992. "Efficacy of Psychology of Mind with dual diagnosed clients." (June). Presentation at 12th Annual Conference of Psychology of Mind, Burlington, VM.

Block, J., and Block, G. 1988. "Longitudinally foretelling drug usage in adolescence: Early childhood personality and environmental precursors." *Child Development* 59: 346-355.

Blumer, H. 1969. *Symbolic Interactionism: Perspective and method*. Englewood Cliffs, NJ: Prentice Hall.

Botkin, J. 1979. *No Limits to Learning: Bridging the human gap*. New York: Pergamon.

Bronfenbrenner, U. 1974. *The Ecology of Human Development*. Cambidge, MA: Harvard University Press.

Brook, J., Gordon, A., Whiteman, M., and Cohen, P. 1986. "Dynamics of Childhood and adolescent personality traits and adolescent drug use." *Developmental Psychology* 22: 403-414.

Brook, J., Nomura, C., and Cohen, P. 1989. "A network of influences on adolescent drug involvement: neighborhood, school, peer, and family." *Genetic, Social and General Psychology Monographs* 115: 303-321.

Brown, I., and Inouye, D. K. 1978. "Learned helplessness through modeling: The rule of perceived similarity in competence." *Journal of Personality and Social Psychology* 36: 900-908.

Burger, P. L., and Luckman, T. 1986. *The Social Construction of Reality*. Garden City, NY: Doubleday.

Carver, C. S., and Scheir, M. F. 1990. "Origins and functions of positive and negative affect: A control-process view." *Psychological Review* 97: 19-35.

Cermak, L. S., and Craik, F. M. 1979 *Levels of Processing in Human Memory*. New York: Wiley.

Chandler, M. J. 1973. "Egocentrism and antisocial behavior: The assessment and training of role-taking and referential communications skills in institutionalized emotionally disturbed children." *Developmental Psychology* 9: 326-337.

Chess, S. 1989. "Defying the voice of doom." T. Dugan and R. Coles eds. *The Child in Our Times*: 179-199. New York: Brunner-Manzel.

Clayton, R. R., and Voss, H. L. 1981. *Young Men and Drugs in Manhattan: A casual analysis*. Rockville, MD: National Institute on Drug Abuse.

Conger, R. D. 1976. "Social control and social learning models of delinquent behavior: A synthesis." *Criminology* 14: 17-40.

Deci, E. L.,& Ryan, R. M. 1991. "A motivational approach to self. Integration in personality." R. Dienstbier ed., *Nebraska Symposium on Motivation: Perspectives on motivation* 38: 237-288. Lincoln, NE: University of Nebraska Press.

Demos, V. 1989. "Resiliency in infancy." T. Dugan and R. Coles eds., *The Child in Our Times: Studies in the development of resiliency*: 3-22). New York: Brunner-Mazel.

Dodge, K. A. 1986. "A social information processing model of social competence in children." M. Perlmutter ed., *Cognitive Perspectives on Children's*

Social and Behavioral Development: The Minnesota symposia on child psychology: 77-125. Hillsdale, NJ: Lawrence Erlbaum Associates.

Dodge, K. A., Murphy, R. M., and Buchsbaum, K. 1984. "The assessment of intention-cue in children: Implications for developmental psychopathology." *Child Development* 55: 163-173.

Elliot, D. S., and Huizinga, D. 1984. *The Relationship Between Delinquent Behavior and Abnormal Problems*. Boulder, CO: Behavioral Research Institute.

Felsman, J. 1989. "Risk and resiliency in childhood: the lives of street children." T. Dugan and R. Coles eds., *The Child in Our Times: Studies in the development of resiliency*:56-80. New York: Brunner-Mazel.

Garmezy, N. 1974. "The study of competence in children at risk for severe psychopathology." E. J. Anthony and C. Koupernik eds., *The Child in his Family: Children at Psychiatric Risk* 3: 77-98. New York: John Wiley and Sons.

Garmezy, N. 1987. "Stress, competence, and development: Continuities in the study of schizophrenic adults and children vulnerable to psychopathology and the search for stress-resistant children." *American Journal of Orthopsychiatry* 57: 159-174.

Garmezy, N. 1991. "Resiliency and vulnerability to adverse developmental outcomes associated with poverty." *American Behavioral Scientist* 34: 416-430.

Garmezy, N., and Rutter, M. 1985. *Stress, Coping and Development in Children*. New York: McGraw Hill.

Harter, S. 1988. "The construction and conservation of the self: James and Cooley revisited." D. K. Lapsley and R. C. Power eds., *Self, Ego, and Identity: Integrative Approaches*: 43-70. New York: Springer-Verlag.

Harter, S. 1990. "Developmental differences in the nature of self-representations: Implications for the understanding, assessment, and treatment of maladaptive behavior." *Cognitive Therapy and Research* 14: 113-142.

Hawkins, J. D., Catalano, R. F., and Miller, J. Y. 1992. "Risk and protective factors for alcohol and other drug problems in adolescence and early adulthood: Implications for substance abuse prevention." *Psychological Bulletin* 112: 64-105.

Howell, F., and Frege, W. 1982. "Early transition into adult roles: Some antecedents and outcomes." *American Educational Research Journal* 19: 51-73.

Iran-Nejad, A. 1990. "Active and dynamic self-regulation of learning processes." *Review of Educational Research* 60: 573-602.

Jessor, R., Chase, J. A., and Donovan, J. E. 1980. "Psychosocial correlates of marijuana use and problem drinking in a national sample of adolescents." *American Journal of Public Health* 70: 604-613.

Kandel, D., Simcha-Fagan, O., and Davies, M. 1986. "Risk factors for delinquency and illicit drug use from adolescence to young adulthood." *The Journal of Drug Issues* 16: 67-90.

Kaplan, H. B., Martin, S. S., and Robbins, C. 1982. "Application of a general theory of deviant behavior: Self derogation and adolescent drug use." *Journal of Health and Social Behavior* 23: 274-294.

Kelly, J. G., Dassoff, N., Levin, I., Schreckengost, J., Stelzner, S. P., and Altman, B. E. 1988. "A guide to conducting prevention research in the community: First steps." *Prevention in Human Services* 6: 1-174.

Lachman, R., Lachman, J., and Butterfield, E. 1979. *Cognitive Psychology and Information Processing*. Hillsdale, NJ: Lawrence Erlbaum.

Linquanti, R. (1992). *Using Community-wide Collaboration to Foster Resilience in Kids: A conceptual framework.* San Francisco: Western Regional Center for Educational Research and Development.

Lochman, J. E., Lampron, L. B., Burch, P. R. and Curry, J. F. (1985). "Client characteristics associated with behavior change for treated and untreated aggressive boys." *Journal of Abnormal Child Psychology* 13: 527-538.

McCombs, B. 1991. "Unraveling motivation: New perspective from research and practice." *The Journal of Experimental Education* 60: 3-14.

McCombs, B. L., and Marzano, R. J. 1990. "Putting the self in self-regulated learning: The self as agent in integrating will and skill." *Educational Psychologist* 25: 51-69.

McCord, J. 1981. "Alcoholism and criminality." *Journal of Studies on Alcohol* 42: 739-748.

McCord, W. and McCord, J. 1959. *Origins of a Crime: A new evaluation of the Cambridge-Somerville study*. New York: Columbia University Press.

Mills, R. C. 1987. "Relationship between school motivational climate, teacher attitudes, student mental health, school failure and health-damaging behavior." (April). Paper presented at the annual meeting of the American Educational Research Association, Washington, DC.

Mills, R. C. 1990. *The Modello/Homestead Gardens Intervention Program: Summary progress report*. (January). Presented at National Association of Counties, Miami, FL.

Mills, R. C. 1991. "A new understanding of self: Affect, state of mind, self understanding, and intrinsic motivation." *Journal of Experimental Education* 60: 67-81.

Mills, R. C. 1991. "Substance abuse, dropout and delinquency prevention: The Modello/ Homestead Gardens Public Housing early intervention project." (June). Paper presented at the 9th annual conference of the Psychology of Mind, St. Petersburg, Fl.

Mills, R. C. 1993. *A Community Empowerment Primer*. Los Angeles, CA: California School of Professional Psychology.

Mills, R. C., Alpert, G., and Dunham, R.1988. "Working with high-risk youth in prevention and early intervention programs: Toward a comprehensive wellness model." *Adolescence* 23: 643-660.

Mills, R. C., Blevins, K. and Pransky, G. 1979. *Toward a New Psychology*. Unpublished manuscript.

Muller, W. 1992. *Legacy of the Heart: The spiritual advantages of a painful childhood*. New York: Simon and Schuster.

Neisser, V. 1976. *Cognitions and Reality*. San Francisco: Freeman.

Nelson, J. 1986. *Understanding*. Rocklin, CA: Prima.

Patterson, G. R. 1982. *Coercive Family Process*. Eugene, OR: Castalia Publishing Company.

Peck, N., Law, A., and Mills, R. C. 1987. *Dropout Prevention: What we learned*. Ann Arbor, MI: Eric Clearinghouse.

Penning, M., and Barnes, G. E. 1982. "Adolescent marijuana use: A review." *International Journal of Addiction* 17: 749-791.

Polk, K., and Kobrin, S. 1972. *Delinquency Prevention Through Youth Development*. Washington, DC: Department of Health, Education and Welfare.

Pransky, G. 1990. *Divorce is Not the Answer*. Blue Ridge Summit, PA: TAB Books.

Ringold, C. A. 1992. *Changing Hearts, Changing Minds: The usefulness of Psychology of Mind in the treatment of paranoid schizophrenia: Two case studies*. Psy.D. Dissertation. Minneapolis, MN: Minnesota School of Professional Psychology.

Rutter, M. 1984. "Resilient children." *Psychology Today* 18 (March): 57-65.

Rutter, M. 1989. "Pathways from childhood to adult life." *Journal of Child Psychology and Psychiatry* 30: 23-51.

Ryan, R. M. 1991. "The nature of the self in autonomy and relatedness." G. R. Goethals and J. Strauss eds., *The Self: Interdisciplinary approaches*: 208-238. New York: Springer-Verlag.

Ryan, R. M., Connel, J. P., and Grolnik, W. S. 1993. "When achievement is not intrinsically motivated: A theory of self-regulation in school." A. K. Boggiano and T. S. Pittman eds., *Achievement and Motivation: A social-developmental perspective*: 167-188. New York: Cambridge University Press.

Ryan, R. M., and Deci, E. L. 1985. "The 'Third Selective Paradigm' and the role of human motivation in cultural and biological selection: A response to Csikszentmihalyi and Massimini." *New Ideas in Psychology* 3: 259-264.

Segal, J. 1986. "Translating stress and coping research into public information and education." M. Kessler and S. E. Goldston eds., *A Decade of Progress in Primary Prevention*: 261-274. Hanover, NH: University Press of New England.

Seligman, M. 1975. *Helplessness: On Depression, Development, and Death.* San Francisco, CA: Freeman.

Selman, R. L. 1976. "Toward a structural analysis of developing interpersonal relations concepts: Research with normal and disturbed pre-adolescent boys." A. D. Pick ed., *Minnesota Symposia on Child Psychology* 10: 156-200. Minneapolis, MN: University of Minnesota Press.

Shantz, C. U. 1975. "Social cognition." E. M. Hetherington, J. W. Hagen, R. Kron, and AH. Stein eds., *Review of Child Development Research* 5: 257-323. Chicago, IL: University of Chicago Press.

Shuford, R.1986. "An exploratory study to determine the effectiveness of a new cognitive treatment approach when used in a clinical setting." Unpublished doctoral dissertation. Eugene, OR: University of Oregon.

Shuford, R., and Crystal, A. 1988. "The efficacy of a neo-cognitive approach to positive psychological change: A preliminary study in an outpatient setting." Paper presented at the Seventh Annual Conference on Psychology of Mind, Coral Gables, FL.

Shure, M., and Spivack, G. 1982. "Interpersonal problem-solving in young children: A cognitive approach to prevention." *American Journal of Community Psychology* 10: 341-356.

Stern, D., and Catterall, J. 1985. "Reducing the high school dropout rate in California: Why we should and how we may." D. Stern, J. Catterall, C. Alhadeff, and M. Ash eds., *Report to the California Policy Seminar on Reducing the Dropout Rate in California*. Berkeley, CA: University of California, School of Education

Stewart, D. 1987. "The efficacy of a neo-cognitive psychology with DUI clients." Paper presented at the Annual Conference of the Florida Alcohol and Drug Abuse Association, Miami, FL.

Suarez, E., and Mills, R. C. 1982. *Sanity, Insanity and Common Sense: The missing link in understanding mental health*. West Allis, WI: Med-Psych Publications.

Suarez, E. M., Mills, R. C., and Stewart, D. 1987. *Sanity, Insanity, and Common Sense: The missing link in understanding mental health* (2nd ed.). New York: Ballantine Books.

Tobler, N. 1986. "Meta-analysis of 143 adolescent drug prevention programs: Quantitative outcome results of program participants compared to a control or comparison group." *Journal of Drug Issues* 16: 537-567.

Today Show, NBC. Segment aired in April 1990 on the Modello/Homestead Gardens Intervention Program.

Wallerstein, J. 1983. "Children of divorce: the psychological tasks of the child." *American Journal of Orthopsychiatry* 53: 230-243.

Werner, E. E. 1986. "Resilient offspring of alcoholics: A longitudinal study from birth to age 18." *Journal of Studies on Alcohol* 44: 34-40.

Werner, E. E. 1989 . "High risk children in young adulthood: A longitudinal study from birth to 32 years." *American Journal of Orthopsychiatry* 59: 71-81.

Werner, E. E., and Smith, R. 1982. *Vulnerable But Invincible: A longitudinal study of resilient children and youth.* New York: Adams, Bannister, and Cox.

West, D. J., and Farrington, D. P.1973. *Who Becomes Delinquent?* London: Heinemann Educational Books.

Wilson, J. Q., and Hernstein, R. J. 1985. *Crime and Human Nature.* New York: Simon and Shuster.

PSYCHOLOGY OF MIND: GLOSSARY OF TERMS

AWARENESS: The thoughts and sensations that we are noticing at any moment in time. Our state of awareness can expand to take in a bigger picture, or can contract to focus more myopically on a person's personal, conditioned view of reality. Our awareness shifts based on whatever thoughts are foremost in our minds and appear compellingly real to us that moment. What we are aware of in our life is a function of the particular mix of conditioned and original thought holding sway in our minds at any time.

COMMON SENSE/MATURITY: An objective, practical and insightful mature, healthy state of mind that is automatically present when the filters of an insecure thought system are not affecting perception. A real, tangible psychological perspective that permits people to see things with more objectivity and a clearer grasp of the long range consequences of their actions. A psychological condition that is experienced as a set of distinct and identifiable qualities; these include maturity, emotional stability, good judgment, intellectual clarity and intuition, creativity, self-confidence, self-esteem and enjoyment of life.

CONDITIONING: A process of cognitive programming and intellectual learning that begins at birth and culminates in a habitual way of thinking about life and about oneself. In addition to useful information on particular skills or information that are helpful, the brain programs in beliefs, ideas, opinions, values, expectations, biases and ingrained assumptions that become an internalized belief system. This belief system is a self confirming, logically consistent frame of reference. In day to day life conditioned beliefs act as a set of psychological filters. These filters in turn shape our perception of reality along the lines of our learned beliefs.

CONDITIONED FRAME OF REFERENCE: A way of looking out at life produced by our learned belief system. This way of looking at life seems real to someone at the time they are immersed in, or at the effect of, this frame of reference. A conditioned frame of reference is produced by our learning from birth; from the beliefs and expectations of our parents, from our culture, extended family, friends, school and educational experiences, from society and the media. A conditioned frame of reference is an illusionary version of reality kept alive in our thinking. When it is in place as a perceptual filter, this frame of reference obscures our innate capacity for common sense and mental clarity.

CONSCIOUSNESS: Ability to experience and see life (i.e., to be aware of reality). The power or ability to make thought images appear real to us via our senses. The additive or ingredient that is mixed with thought to produce each person's subjective psychological reality. Combining consciousness with thought culminates in that person's thoughts taking on the appearance of reality.

EGO: A self image made up of our conditioned thoughts of who and what we are. Our self concept. How we define ourselves in relation to others. Conditioned thoughts from the past that include what we think we need to be happy, successful, liked, admired or worthwhile. These thoughts comprise that part of our make-up that makes our well-being contingent on external events. The ego, as an image of self importance in the external world, forces us to prove ourselves leading to insecurity which results in the feelings of fear, jealousy, hate, anger and greed.

EMOTIONS: A psychic and physical reaction. To move away from or out of a state of well being (equilibrium); to disturb. A state that prepares the organism, both physically and mentally for immediate action. Internally generated, momentary reactions to thoughts which can obscure deeper positive feelings. Emotions may be positive or negative but are always stimulated by thought. When emotions are not signalling real danger (physical) to the organism, they act as an indicator of the level of insecurity (level of understanding) at any point in time. When a person is functioning with more insecurity, their emotions will be more negative; in more secure states, more positive.

EMPOWERMENT: The ability of people to free themselves from conditioned habits of thinking. Empowerment first involves people recognizing that they have deeper positive psychological capacities that transcend their conditioning, their circumstances, or their past traumas or behavior patterns. Accessing these capacities frees people from the limitations of their past, accesses self respect, hope and insights, engaging productive and assertive states of mind. Engaging these capacities better equips people to work collectively and individually to change adverse social or economic conditions.

FEELINGS: In P.O.M., used with a capital (Feelings) to allude to deeper, unconditional, positive feelings that come with higher levels of understanding such as: love, gratitude, serenity, peace of mind, creativity, happiness, wonder, appreciation, joy. The other type of feelings are those produced by our conditioned thoughts (see emotions above). Higher order (F)eelings are produced by original thoughts that comprise the awakened background of life that produce what people call peak experiences, or non-contingent enjoyment of life, universal feelings that are available to everyone and are a constant part of the experience of higher levels of understanding. These feelings are indicators of mental health.

INNOCENCE: The psychological fact that everyone is doing their best, given how things look to them. This term refers to how people become a prisoner of their learned frame of reference when they are seeing things through the filters of their conditioned ways of thinking. At these times, the person's thoughts are leading them to believe they must act the way they do in order to survive or protect their self concept. Their resulting perceptions appear logical and accurate to the person when they are functioning in insecure states of mind.

INSECURITY: The generalized emotion of fear or anxiety that something is wrong, or could go wrong. Any form of the thought that "I will not be (am not) all right, happy, or accepted unless I do something the right way, the way that is correct" (within the person's belief system). Thoughts that cause a person's sense of well being or survival being perceived as being at risk. Their perceptions then become systematically negatively distorted leading to even more negative emotions such as fear, restlessness, anger, paranoia, frustration, guilt, and self-pity. Thoughts become increasingly centered around feelings of self-consciousness, blame, hopelessness and negativity toward their surroundings.

INSIGHT: The experience of seeing or realizing something new; of gaining an understanding of life and how thought works that is beyond our current way of thinking. Insights are generated internally, from the natural, innate intelligence that is produced directly from Mind, without the interference of conditioned thought. Insights shift our vantage point or frame of reference to provide solutions to problems that baffled us prior to that time. An insight is a realization that leads to a deeper understanding of any situation, to wisdom, clarity and effective action. A genuine insight is accompanied by positive feelings, as it brings solutions and revives hope, compassion and motivation.

LEVEL OF UNDERSTANDING: Defines a continuum determined by the degree to which a person realizes the role that thought plays in everyday life. The person's level of understanding also defines the range of their feeling states. These states extend from extremely insecure, paranoid or hostile states of mind in which the individual is caught up in the effects of their separate, conditioned frame of reference to a higher state of mental health where the person is more aware of the role of thought. At higher levels of understanding, the person grasps how thought works to create our unique personal experience as human beings. At higher levels of understanding the individual more effortlessly and spontaneously experiences their innate wisdom as well as higher order feelings such as love, compassion, joy, happiness and understanding.

LISTENING: Used in this paradigm with a capital (L) means to hear beyond the apparent, or conditioned belief system. Listening for an insight or realization that helps us understand another person's reality. Listening with a small (l) in this paradigm means listening to judge whether what we are hearing confirms our conditioned thinking (What we already think). True (L)istening is a creative process. Reflective, diffuse, open to something new and unknown. Alludes to an inner, curious, respectful listening and receptivity, leading to listening better to others to hear and understand how another is seeing and experiencing reality. Listening involves receptivity to insight. It entails dropping preconceptions and expectations and hearing with an open or quiet mind.

MENTAL HEALTH: Psychological perspective or vantage point where people can see the connection between thought and their experience of life. A natural and continuously accessible tangible state of mind that can be moved into directly regardless of people's past, their history of emotional disturbance, or present situation. Characterized by positive feelings and high self-esteem in which people access their inborn common sense and wisdom. Emerges from within the individual as a package of attributes that have been associated in the literature with resiliency, self esteem, self efficacy and positive motivation.

MIND: A universally held psychic "power" source that continuously projects thought and consciousness outward to create the appearance of reality. Totality of all intelligence. The source of a universasl capacity for psychological insights separate from the individual thought system. The intelligence and origin behind consciousness and thought.

PSYCHOLOGY: Originally, the study of the mind/psyche/soul. The original word means the logic of the soul. Today this term refers to an overall understanding of human behavior as it derives from human mental functioning. The fundamental parameters of psychology in this paradigm, (P.O.M.), are Mind, a universal intelligence, Consciousness, the vehicle or conduit for experiencing reality and Thought, the minute to minute formulator of reality.

SELF ESTEEM: A natural feeling of well being and self respect that emerges automatically when the individual is not in an insecure, self conscious frame of mind. A non-conditional sense of self worth and self acceptance that contributes to higher levels of wisdom, to a positive outlook and motivation to learn and do the best at anything we take on in life. This natural psychological state is in place in everyone prior to their learning a conditioned self concept. It can be reengaged and brought to the surface at any time and cannot be lost.

SELF CONCEPT: A learned concept of who we are, what we like and don't like, what we are good at and not good at, what we need to have or to live up to in order to be happy. Self concept is learned via cognitive programming from our family, our culture, our exposure to societal beliefs and biases. Learned as part of our thought system. A self concept is the result of the process of conditioning, and is held in place at lower levels of understanding by insecurity.

STATES OF MIND: A qualitative description of the moment to moment quality and nature of people's thoughts and perceptions. Combining Thought with Consciousness leads to the observed emotional states of mind composed of beliefs leading to perception, emotions and consequently, behavior. Behavior stems from thought; in insecure states of mind our behavior is produced by separate conditioned realities (i.e., individual thought systems), or in secure states of mind by insights, wisdom and common sense. A person's state of mind will vary over time along the dimension, or continuum of degrees of insecure thinking; from a more common sense or mentally healthy state of mind to a more insecure, negative state. A person's moment to moment state of mind is determined by their level of understanding of the role of thought in relationship to their daily or even momentary experience, and their mood level at the moment.

THOUGHT: The psychological vehicle that transmits reality to the brain. Thought is projected outward using the "psychic" or psychological power of "Mind." Combining the two elements, Thought with Consciousness, the mind formulates each individual's perception of reality. The universal psychological function, thinking, produces specific thoughts that determine every human beings experience of life moment to moment. Thought works through each of our five senses, from stimuli in the environment to (1) transmit images into our brains and (2) create images within our heads that interpret these external stimuli (give them a subjective meaning). This function involves creating reality second by second as a continuous flow of thought; the content of thought can either be negative or positive. Whether thinking is negative or positive depends on the level of understanding at which the individual is functioning.

THOUGHT SYSTEM: A learned way of looking at and interpreting life. An internally consistent set of beliefs that make logical sense to that individual, but do not make sense in the same way to anyone else. Each person's learned, unique, subjective view of life. A set of beliefs which differs across individuals but to which each person attaches their sense of well being and survival. A set of psychological filters which interfere with wisdom and block our capacity for understanding.

UNDERSTANDING: Describes the result of seeing clearly the role thought plays in everyday life. Recognizing how thought, at different levels of understanding determines how someone sees life. Understanding is accompanied by compassion, a lack of judgment or blame, a sense of how to help in a positive, gentle way and a recognition of how to stay out of trouble by avoiding the pitfalls of our own conditioned belief system.

WISDOM: A psychological perspective that is available to everyone before the contents of their conditioned beliefs. Wisdom is a source of insights and mental clarity that allows us to see the best possible solution to the problem at hand: the solution that helps everyone the most, that is the most generally beneficial, compassionate and that leads to the most productive outcomes. Our own wisdom also shows us the role that thought plays in everyday life. It is also a faculty that helps us to distinguish between valid insights and conditioned reactions to situations in our lives.